MY LIFE

MY LIFE

NORMAN A. DE BRUYNE FRS

MIDSUMMER BOOKS

FOR MY WIFE ELMA

First published in Great Britain in 1996
by Midsummer Books,
an imprint of Silent Books Ltd
Swavesey, Cambridge CB4 5QG

ISBN 1 85183 080 4

British Library Cataloguing-in-Publication Data.
A catalogue record for this book is available from the
British Library.

Printed in Great Britain by
Redwood Books, Trowbridge, Wiltshire.

Front end papers
left AERO field, Duxford 1934
right CIBA Duxford, present day

Back end papers
left Norman de Bruyne, 1941
right Elma de Bruyne, 1935

Drawings by Jane de Glehn

CONTENTS

ACKNOWLEDGEMENTS

I wish to express my grateful thanks to the numerous people, friends and colleagues for all their help and advice, in particular for permission to use photographs from CIBA, Boeing Publicity Department, Express Plastics of Norfolk, The Royal Institution of Great Britain, The Royal Society, Trinity College Library and Mr & Mrs R Bradney for the photograph of Mrs Tipper

For the continual encouragement from Sir Arthur Marshall and Richard Clarkson, for permission to quote from speeches and publications of Sir Michael Atiyah, Richard Clarkson and Dr Elizabeth Garnsey.

For the practical help of Jill and Jonathan Steinberg, Sheila of 'Keystrokes', George & Kathleen Newell, Peter Fluck and 'Silent Books' for indulging a ninety plus year old!

For the wonderful work by Clare Orchard, my editor, and most importantly to Peggy Thompson for her patience and help and without whom the manuscript would not have reached the publishers.

For the friendship and love of the late Robert Lea, 'Bobby' and Loulou Marsh.

FOREWORD

A PROFILE

NORMAN ADRIAN DE BRUYNE is probably the only man who ever gave up being the Junior Bursar of Trinity College, Cambridge, to become a glue maker. If anyone is tempted hastily to condemn that as a piece of sordid commercialism, let him suspend judgement until he shall learn what sort of glue it was, and who was responsible for turning a young researcher's footsteps from the path of revolutionary aircraft design towards glue. Young de Bruyne's trouble was that he was essentially an individualist, forced away from doing things himself for the sheer satisfaction of achievement, by the hard facts of economic life.

Nevertheless, when he turned away from structures to new ways of sticking them together, aeronautics lost a brilliant designer. By one of life's ironies, it was Geoffrey de Havilland who turned him away and sent him off to start hotting up his almost primitive glue-pots in a corner of a Cambridgeshire field where now stands an imposing factory as a memorial to his surrender – a surrender tinged, one suspects, with that same impish delight in doing something a little outrageous which had moved him to build an aeroplane he knew could not get an airworthiness certificate and then getting one for it after uprooting the very foundations of British safety regulations.

That little four-seater low-wing monoplane ought really to have been preserved and embalmed as a reminder to all young men that red tape can be cut and stuffy, safety-first civil service scientists can be converted. The name he chose for it was a challenge. He called it the Snark. There was nothing abnormal about its shape or form. The wing section indeed was that used in the Hendy Heck. All the revolutionary things were in the structure, both wings and fuselage. Neither, by the standards of the Royal Aircraft Establishment

(RAE), was strong enough. When de Bruyne submitted his plans they were rejected.

Those were the days of the biplane. The RAE was still working on the assumption that each wing spar had to bear the various loads independently and was prescribing strength factors accordingly. This young Cambridge don in 1931 was proposing to put such a stiff covering on his monoplane wing that the two spars would be virtually bonded into a single unit. He had also designed his wing entirely in wood, and the strength of such a structure was underrated by the RAE formulae. From the RAE's point of view he had been just as criminally optimistic in stressing his fuselage.

In this he had applied the Wagner tension field analysis, which dealt with the behaviour of beams of such a depth that the webs crinkle elastically under load. The RAE was not prepared to accept this young German's dictum translated into a wooden monocoque fuselage; and a furious argument developed. Temperatures were brought down when the superintendent was persuaded by K.T. Spencer, now chief scientist of the Ministry of Fuel and Power, to buy a fuselage from de Bruyne for testing to destruction. That settled the argument magnificently in de Bruyne's favour.

Not only did the Snark get its certificate of airworthiness but ultimately, in Reports and Memoranda, 1694, the RAE publicly confessed its sins of omission and altered its stressing methods. At the age of 27 this youngster had pushed a Government establishment along the road of progress. The feat must stand unique in the annals. He of course got a certain amount of mischievous satisfaction out of it. There were no signs of apprehension in him while the row boiled up. With a grin of complete selfassurance he had gone ahead on the building of the Snark in one of Marshall's hangars at Cambridge while the heat of his bombshell dissipated itself.

At first he had a ground engineer and two boys to help him. Then the ground engineer left for a better job and de Bruyne himself qualified as a ground engineer and even became an Airworthiness Inspection Department approved welder. So, designer and ground engineer in one, he saw the job through and at the end of three years the Snark flew. With its thick wing it flew so well that those who were unfamiliar with it usually had a job to get it on the ground again. When de Bruyne had finished with it, Professor (later Sir) Bennett Melvill Jones took it over for some of the earliest detailed experiments in airflow with tufts of wool stuck on various parts of the wing. In the early days of the war it passed into the hands of three technical journalists, the late F. D. Bradbrooke, Peter Masefield and Thurston James.

Two years before the Snark was finished, de Bruyne had turned himself into the Cambridge Aeroplane Construction Co. He had already done some work on plastics and published a paper on the creep stress of certain plastic materials. He was hoping to bring new materials as well as new structures to the service of aircraft design, but funds trickled away and debts began to build up. By the spring of 1932, the financial situation was becoming serious and at that point Geoffrey de Havilland appeared on the scene. He wanted research done on plastics for aircraft and was ready to start de Bruyne off with £1,000.

The association with the de Havilland company determined de Bruyne's subsequent course. In 1934 he moved from Cambridge to a field at Duxford. That field was intended to become his aerodrome and indeed it did. In a corner of it he set up a little corrugated iron shed for the production of his ureaformaldehyde resin and went to work. Within a year he had produced a wing rib made of reinforced synthetic resin and a new and more ambitious aeroplane was on the way to succeed the Snark – but other ideas, including the development of honeycomb sandwich materials, were sizzling. These pointed to the importance of bonding, and glues to serve that end demanded more and more attention. The company grew. That same year it became Aero Research Ltd., and although de Bruyne could not foresee it, he was doomed from that moment to be a maker of glues.

From the bonding of wooden structures, he and his new associates were to move on to the bonding of metals in 1943. Redux the glue they developed for that purpose, is now in wide and increasing use. He declares that he was driven in the end to build up the glue side of the business by the 'fickleness of officialdom'. In 1942 the Ministry of Aircraft Production had tried to turn his establishment into a Government plastics laboratory, and when he rebelled, had withdrawn all support and removed all the research apparatus and plant to the RAE. De Bruyne saved his bacon by getting sub-contract work for aircraft repairs; and hitting on Redux saved his sanity. A long time was to pass before it showed a profit. Yet in that year of 1943 there was a profit on the other glues.

It meant nothing because the company had never made a profit in peace time, and so was subject to 100 per cent excess profits tax. None of the financial people thought anything of his prospects and no backing for post-war expansion was to be had. The managing director was forced to take another plucky step to get his glue production ready for the market he knew must arise. As excess profits tax was collected a year in arrear, he spent one whole year's contribution on a spray drying plant. The gamble came off. The market for his glues was waiting. And in 1946 the Swiss firm CIBA put up enough money to secure for it a majority share in Aero Research. The managing director remains the same. He no longer does the research himself, although he directs and inspires it. As he says, quoting Sir William Bragg, 'for research you must have no pre-occupations' – and a managing director is much pre-occupied with administration. His erstwhile aerodrome is now the site of a big up-to-date factory.

In November (1957) Norman de Bruyne will be 53. He might be regarded by some as set in his ways with his major triumphs behind him. In one of his temperament and stock that is a dangerous presumption. He comes of Dutch stock on his father's side and of Bristol missionary stock on his mother's. His father was intended to follow the family profession of medicine in Holland. Finding that not to his taste, he gathered together his assets and set out to do some pioneering in Tierra del Fuego. There, on the shores of the Magellan Straits, he married a descendant of one of the original Bristol missionaries and there his four sons were born while his sheep farming and his not too profitable whaling expeditions were established.

When the boys were old enough for school he brought them to England, spending half of each year here and half on his big farm in South America. Norman and another brother went to Lancing and the third to Wellington. In due course Norman arrived at Cambridge and a mere second in Part I of the Natural Science Tripos persuaded him that 'in future I should have to do my own instruction'. Part 2 got him a first. A subsequent year's research led to his election as a Fellow of his own college. He went on with research and took his doctor's degree. And meanwhile he had been taken for a flight in a Moth belonging to another Fellow of the college. That was what turned his mind to aircraft structures and, by a twist of fortune, landed him in glue.

He avers that, as a late developer, he would not get his chance at Cambridge in these days, when examinations determine the selection of undergraduates. Those who know him best believe that what he calls development was really an intensely independent and questing spirit; and they do not for a moment consider that it has been quenched by glue.

The *New Scientist*, 10 October 1957

INTRODUCTION

I WISH I could match the entrancing and portentous opening of Alexander Herzen's mighty memoirs – 'Oh, please, Nurse tell me again how the French came to Moscow!'

It encouraged me to write this account of my antics on the tight rope of time (the dimension along which we can travel in one direction only) by his initial remarks in *The Pole Star* (1855):

> In order to write one's reminiscences it is not at all necessary to be a great man, nor a notorious criminal, nor a celebrated artist, nor a statesman – it is quite enough to be simply a human being, to have something to tell and not merely to desire to tell it but at least have some ability to do so.

Looking back I discern a principle in my life-style which to others may be enigmatic. For instance my sister-in-law asked, 'Norman, why do you always leave a job as soon as you have made a success of it?' and when I emigrated to USA in 1967, Dr Robert Kappeli (Chairman of CIBA) who called me 'Diogenes' wrote, 'I am always glad to receive news from you and try to puzzle out what is really on your mind which I hasten to assure you I find an intriguing and rewarding one.' My economist friend Professor Tullio Bagiotti said to me, 'You serve a hard master Norman – yourself.' My basic principle is a simple one; I move when I see that my freedom is endangered. There is nothing noble or idealistic in such a principle; but without freedom I cannot invent or discover, and as Claude Bernard (1813-73) said, 'The joy of discovery is certainly the liveliest that the mind of man can ever feel.' I do not ask, as some of my Cambridge colleagues did, for freedom from the rules of common morality; but I greatly value freedom from the arbitracy will or actions of persons or institutions (cf. F. A. Hayek).[1] Naturally one

1. F. A. Hayek, *The Constitution of Liberty*, London 1976, p. 284.

must be careful not to allow this freedom to degenerate into the demand 'Be reasonable; do it my way.'

My life long friend and colleague the late Robert Lea read me these words adapted from Emily Brontë when I left CIBA in 1961:

Often rebuked yet always back returning
To those first feelings that were born with me
And leaving busy chase of wealth and learning
For dreams that live in new discovery
I'll walk where my own nature would be leading
It vexes me to choose another guide
From all the seeds it's my own choice to find a seedling
And bring the sense of new achievement to my side.

I am a physicist who became an aeronautical engineer who became an entrepreneur and ended up by making laboratory instruments; and in my own way I have enjoyed and am still enjoying myself hugely, although saddened by the decline of the country which gave me so much but has turned away from the principles which made it great (cf. Margaret Gowing).[2]

Dr Alan L. Mackay remarks in his book of quotations *The Harvest of a Quiet Eye* (of which I have made good use in this autobiography): 'Being a scientist resembles membership of a religious order and a scientist usually finds that he has more in common with a colleague on the other side of the world than with his next door neighbour.'[3] Any non-scientist who marries a scientist should be warned that a scientist always has a second love in his or her life. I married a good cellist and that has worked out rather well because it gives each of us a second love. My wife is a member of the remarkable Monod family who are French protestants and through her I got to know many delightful friends including Jacques Monod who was both scientist and cellist. Incidentally Gabriel Monod, the historian, married Herzen's daughter Olga – hence my interest in Herzen.

What sets a scientist apart from others? A scientist is perhaps more acutely aware of the difficulty of arriving at the truth than most people, because life in a laboratory is a continuous struggle

2. Margaret Gowing, 'Science, Technology and Education: England in 1870', the Wilkins Lecture 1976, *Notes and Records of the Royal Society,* Vol. 32 (1977–8), pp. 71–90.
3. Alan L. Mackay, The Harvest of a Quiet Eye: A Selection of Scientific Quotations, (ed. Maurice Ebison), Bristol, 1977.

against gremlins; on the other hand an engineer carries more direct responsibility than a scientist because an engineer has to produce hardware on which people's lives may depend. The challenge is greatest in space travel, but even the design of subsonic aircraft can be an exercise in achieving the almost impossible. Dr MacCready's 'Gosamer Albatross' is a perfect example, which despite its frailty is a paradigm for the intelligent use of the new composite materials from which aircraft are now built.

Lord Zuckerman wrote:

> Sadly I find that I have outlived most of the people who come into my story. All the hopes which they personified, all their needs, all that pleasure enjoyed and given, all that pain endured, all that knowledge stored in so many heads, gone forever.[4]

This is true of my story too, but it is some consolation that their constructive work has been passed on to the next generation who will build on it. This is surely one of the clearest distinctions between mankind and the other animals.

I was born in Punta Arenas, Chile, a former settlement for convicts, and to explain how that came about I must begin with my paternal grandfather Job Kosten de Bruyne who was the doctor in Zierikzee on the remote island of Schouwen in what was then a primitive part of the Netherlands. He took his degree in medicine at Leyden on 26 January 1845; I have his dissertation (printed in Latin). One thesis was that all cure of sickness is due to nature, art is only its helpmate and heals only through it. An excellent thesis and especially at a time when there were no anaesthetics, asepsis, antibiotics, x-rays, bacteriology, cardiographs, hypodermic syringes, no vaccines except for smallpox, and no blood transfusions. In 1842, the mortality rate after major amputations in nine leading Paris hospitals was 52 per cent My father was expected to follow in the footsteps of my grandfather and was registered at the University of Groningen in 1886;[5] but the study of medicine did not appeal to him and he made friends with a group of wealthy students. The outcome was that my grandfather handed him the equivalent of about thirty pounds and told him to leave home. Cut off in this dramatic fashion he thought of the French branch of the family

4. Lord Zuckerman, *From Apes to Warlords 1904–6,* London 1978, p. xiii.
5. For this information I am indebeted to Mr Koops, curator, Rijks Universiteit, Groningen.

which had originated from an elopement with an officer in Napoleon's army in 1799. He spent some time in their tannery at Vendôme and acquired an excellent knowledge of French which enabled him to become a guide at the Paris exhibition of 1889 (for which the Eiffel Tower was built) and correspondent for a Dutch paper. He then decided to emigrate to South America and with money borrowed from his brother-in-law he got a passage to Buenos Aires where he bought two hundred cattle and drove them southward. Eventually he reached Punta Arenas and the Straits of Magellan; there he prospered. He opened a store, became a director of the Bank of Punta Arenas,[6] Netherlands consul, head of the fire brigade, a sheep farmer, brought the first refrigerated ship for transport of mutton to Europe (it was called the *Beurre Frais*), started a whaling company bringing crew and ships from Norway. He fell off his horse one day and was taken into a missionary where his clothing was repaired by a strikingly attractive English girl named Maud Mattock. He asked her whether she would be willing to sew on his buttons for the rest of her life and they were married on 6 August 1895 and had four children, all boys.

Albert Sylvester	1896-1908	(Died of TB)
Henry Bernard Arthur	1898-1976	Married Mary E. Hayward (2 daughters, 2 sons)
Gordon	1900-72	Married Rosamond Knox
Norman Adrian	1904 –	Married Elma L. Marsh (1 daughter, 1 son)

We were all born in Punta Arenas and by Chilean law were Chilean subjects but my father stamped my birth certificate with the Netherlands consular seal no doubt to establish my 'Dutchness'.

After 1906 we lived in Redhill, Surrey, England and my father spent each English summer there with wife and children and each Patagonian summer by himself on the estancia 'Rio Verde'. Bernard took over 'Rio Verde' in 1930. It was alas expropriated by the Communist Allende in 1970. Gordon joined the British army and rose to the rank of Brigadier in the 60th Rifles.

6. *The Standard* (No. 29, 13 April 1908) – a British newspaper published in Punta Arenas – has an advertisement for the Bank of Punta Arenas mentioning P. A. de Bruyne as one of the directors.

CHAPTER ONE

LITTLEHAMPTON

BERNARD was suffering increasingly from asthma and on our doctor's advice we decided to move from Redhill to Littlehampton in Sussex in 1910.

Being now 6 years old my memories become somewhat clearer. We spent our last night at Redhill at Laker's Hotel close to the Redhill railway station (where Gordon's friend Mr Welfare worked) and then we took the London Brighton and South Coast Railway to Littlehampton (LBSCR). The LBSCR, like all British railways at that time, was a public company which year after year paid dividends after keeping its track and rolling stock in excellent clean condition. It competed with the London Chatham and Dover Railway (London Smash 'em & Turnover Railway), had its own distinctive colours and uniforms and was regarded as an excellent investment for widows and orphans. It pioneered electric suburban trains with overhead wires unaffected by ice. The engine drivers took pride in their locomotives and kept all the brasswork shining brightly. We boys knew that only 'foreigners' had profitless railways owned by the state and whose trains ran on tracks which were lengths of steel spiked straight down on to the sleepers – not sitting proudly on chairs held in place with wooden wedges. And continental guards blew ridiculous little horns when they wanted their trains to go. In England the railways made their own locomotives, which were said to be better than the Beyer Peacock ones we exported to the whole world. Bernard had 'bagged' (adopted) the London North Eastern, Gordon had the Great Western and I had to take the Midland, which claimed to be the most comfortable one and was the first to introduce United States Pullman cars. Undoubtedly, Gordon had made the best choice. He also bagged Harrods and later on I had to make do with Selfridge's, which admittedly served the best ice creams but was a bit of an upstart and had lifts manned by girls in riding dress complete with high boots and whips.

Father bought leasehold (and later, freehold) of a corner house in Fitzalan Road, opposite the Carnegie Free Library. It was larger than the Redhill house and had a stable and carriage house. We had a horse called Danilo and a brougham and a dog cart; Mr Harwood, the coachman, wore a top hat when driving the brougham. Danilo was drafted into the army soon after August 1914 and we got a Daimler with a sleeve-valve engine in his place. The Carnegie Free Library was useful because it took the *English Mechanic.* The librarian blacked out all the racing results in the daily papers as he disapproved of betting and the kind of clientele which it attracted to his library. The books were pretty useless as very few had been added since 1908. Nevertheless, I found the early novels of H. G. Wells; one I specially liked was *When the Sleeper Awakes.* But my greatest discoveries in the Free Library were Samuel Smiles' *Lives of the Engineers* and Mark Twain's *A Connecticut Yankee in King Arthur's Court.*

We all went to school at Wellesley House, and were known officially as de Bruyne major, minor and minimus. It was the only preparatory school in Littlehampton willing to take dayboys; the other two schools regarded this as clear evidence of our inferiority. Our headmaster, Mr Frank Rowe, was a former classical scholar of Trinity College, Cambridge, and an excellent cricketer. Mrs Rowe's maiden name was Waddington; she was, I believe, an aunt of the future Professor Waddington. They started a special junior class, which I attended, and engaged a nice school-marm called Miss Gunston to run it. I was a slow learner and could not read until I was 8 years old; when I realised that shops had names that identified them, this struck me as a good idea! I can see Miss Gunston in a photo before me wearing a hat. In the bottom left-hand corner sitting cross-legged is a cheerful cherub called Passmore, who lived next-door-but-one to us and who afterwards became Abbot or Head of Downside School. Next to him is Noel Cuppage, whom I regarded as milk sop, but when I challenged him to tie his own boots he did so at lightning speed by a French technique that I only learned at the age of 36 from my wife. I am in the extreme bottom right-hand corner and next to me is Clarkson minor who bullied me; my father told me to hit back and it so surprised him that he left me alone thereafter. Clarkson major (not in the photo) lent me his parachute for the trials of my aeroplane at Martlesham some twenty-five years later. Next to Clarkson minor are the twins (one of them was later knighted) with their elder brother and next to him (looking down) was a pathetic character. He was always dressed in 'reach-me downs' and apparently was related to Mrs Rowe, who was forever disapproving of him. I was a favourite of Mrs Rowe, who called me 'The human being' because when a German princess inspected the school she addressed me as 'My little man'. I repudiated her insinuation and when asked, 'What are you then?' I replied, 'A human being.' But Gordon complained that Mrs Rowe was always 'throwing up windows' at him and leaning out and screaming 'Gordon tell your mother' this or that.

There were three classrooms not counting Miss Gunston's tiny room. The biggest was used as a living room and for evening prayers, at which time Mrs Rowe played the harmonium. On the wall was a huge map of the world in Mercator's projection. The British Empire was coloured pink; the map was practically all pink although Egypt was permitted to have pink stripes. I mentally established a claim to Russia as it seemed to be the only country of any size left and my brothers did not want it.

Mr Rowe told us that the British Empire was the biggest empire that had ever existed, but that some people said it would end like the Roman Empire, broken up by the insatiable demands of the Romans for free bread and circuses. Mr Rowe said it was the great hope of the Indian Civil Service that eventually the Indians would be able to run that country themselves. He also told us that there were two ways by which mankind had acquired knowledge: firstly by revelation, secondly by observation. He used to say 'Laborare est orare' and this came in useful in later life when the rector of Duxford upbraided me for working on Sundays. Mr Kingdom, the assistant master, sitting closest to me was a hero because he owned an 'Indian' motorcycle. (Triumph in present day jargon). One day in class he said to me 'Hold that grin de Bruyne' and came down and measured its length. He left his dog with me to look after in the summer holidays and when he came back he told me that his parents thought it was time for him to make a career for himself and so he was going to join the Air Force. This was, of course, before World War I; he was killed in that war and so was his successor, Mr Barltrop. It was well known at the time that the average life of a pilot on the Western Front was three weeks.

Mr and Mrs Rowe were devoted, but not narrow-minded, members of the Church of England and this did not prevent them from having two Siamese of unknown religions and three Roman Catholics in the school. We used to have visits from various Church of England clergymen from the 'Black Country' which seemed to be a dreadful area, where the factories were so close-packed that on weekdays there was hardly any sunlight; I always enjoyed these lectures as they were accompanied by lantern slides projected by limelight. This consisted of a cylinder of lime heated by an oxy-hydrogen flame. There was no electricity in Littlehampton at that time. I used bichromate cells for my experiments. One had to lower a zinc electrode into the electrolyte of sodium bichromate and sulphuric acid and one got 1.8 volts and quite a lot of amperes out of each cell.

We all trooped off each Sunday to Littlehampton Parish Church – a Wesbyterian-looking building of 1840 or so with staircases and a gallery and a later addition at the east end, possibly added as a result of an outbreak of 'Newmania'.

Mr Rowe did not sit with us but came in with the choirboys who seemed to be dressed in black skirts and nightshirts. Mrs Rowe must have regarded our presence in church partly as a public relations exercise for Wellesley House and she handed out lozenges of compressed sugar and paraformaldehyde in the hope that they would prevent us coughing – there was, of course, no such thing as central heating and we all suffered from the cold and from 'chilblains'.

The younger ones among us were, I believe, allowed to leave before the sermon but I remember one sermon which diminished my respect for the vicar. He was arguing the case for God from the orderliness of nature, particularly the wonders of gravitation which extended to the furthest corners of the universe and to the smallest particles we could see. 'Consider this particle of dust on my spectacles' he said. 'What is holding it there? Gravitation, of course.' At Sunday lunch I asked my father about this and he confirmed that gravitation had nothing to do with holding the dust in place on the rector's eyeglasses. But it was only many years later that I learned what held the dust in place.

G. H. Hardy told me many years later that he had experienced a similar loss of confidence when the Bishop of London preached a sermon and said that he had recently been out in a fog and seen a boy flying a kite. The boy could not see the kite but knew it was there by the tug on the string. That was what faith was all about; we cannot see God, but we are held to Him by the thread of faith.

The sidesman in the church was the Littlehampton carpenter, Mr Norris. He took the bag round for the collection, wore a black gown and emitted deafening 'Amens' to encourage the congregation to respond to the prayers sent out by the vicar. I was not too sure about the effectiveness of prayer and asked my darling nursemaid-plus-house-maid called Florence Killick ('Florence' was arbitrarily imposed on her by my mother, who considered 'Ann', which was her real name, to be 'common') to pray that my father's pince-nez would come off the next time he smacked me and she did and they did. Then the vicar told us a story of how he had prayed for rain, having told the congregation he was going to do so. When they came out of church it was raining but the only person with an umbrella was an 8 year old girl. This encouraged me to pray for wet weather in the afternoon to avoid having to play football, hockey or cricket. This appeared to be fairly successful, but it was not until I read a biography of Pasteur that I learned of the importance of controls.

Before church we learned the 'Catechism' which began with 'What is your name? N or M.' The answer was not 'Norman',which was puzzling; even more puzzling was the command not to come at your neighbour's wife. A boy named Luchow was lucky enough to escape all this nonsense because he was a Roman Catholic and surprisingly was allowed to paste pictures of actresses in his scrapbook.

In the summer Mr Rowe took us down to the far east end of the seashore beyond the end of the parade (very wise of him) and we bathed. I dreaded this because the brothers Smart enjoyed holding my head under water. Mr Rowe saw them doing it once and said, 'I am ashamed of you' and they desisted but I was too frightened ever to learn to swim.

Intellectual life at Littlehampton was not on a high level; I did not realise how limited my vocabulary was until I encountered J. F. Roxburgh at Lancing, and I suppose it was not until I met Littlewood and Hardy at Trinity College, Cambridge that I heard good English conversation for the first time. As children our reading was confined to comic papers such as *Rainbow* where the exploits of Tiger Tim at Mrs Bruin's school are still firmly implanted in my mind. He was a friendly tiger like the Princeton tiger unleashed by Exxon on the world many years later ('Put a tiger in your tank'). Another memorable character was Professor Radium in *Puck.* I met him later at Cambridge in real life. We took the *Daily Graphic,* a picture paper in tabloid form, originally intended to be a woman's daily paper. It was similar to, but not as vulgar as, the *Daily Mirror* and I chiefly remember it by its weather forecasts portrayed by a classical lady hiding under a classical Greek umbrella when it rained or a classical Greek parasol when it was sunny; her credibility was at least as good as the Old Moore's Almanac studies in the kitchen. Later I picked up an interest in astronomy from a monthly feature in the *Daily Telegraph* and in radio from articles in the *Scout* which was taken by Gordon who also sometimes bought *Answers* whose full title was *Answers to Correspondents.* It was a mine of information, much of it the kind to be found in the *Guinness Book of Records* and it also helped readers with personal problems such as 'My boyfriend looks embarrassed when I talk about engagement rings. What should I do?' Then there was *Punch* in which George Belcher specialised in the malaprops of charwomen and there were jokes about small boys and old gents ending 'collapse of old gentleman.' The traditional joke was about a bishop lecturing a page boy, 'Who is it who is so mighty that even I am of no significance?' 'The Missus sir.' Mr Rowe said that Bernard ought to read good English literature and Father bought a complete set of Dickens. The surnames put me off; they seemed such a crude unrealistic way of portraying character and the pictures by Cruickshank looked flyblown and repulsive. I ploughed through *Great Expectations* and then gave up.

My brothers and I started our own Sunday weekly called the *Weekly Herald* and continued it for years. It was a spoof on the real thing. Dr C. R. Burch once said to me that as adults we do successfully what we tried to do in childhood and I think it is true; it is rather surprising that after such journalistic activity none of us took to journalism as a career.

The town of Littlehampton was owned by the Duke of Norfolk, who lived at Arundel in a romantic castle built in eighteenth century Gothic style by an amateur architect ancestor. Our cook, Kitty, got friendly with one of the staff and he took Kitty and me all round the battlements. The river Arun ran out to the sea at Littlehampton, officially described as 'The Port of Arundel', carrying all the sewage with it which on the return tide was washed back onto the seashore adjacent to the mouth of the river. The smell was attributed to seaweed. There was a short pier with a miniature lighthouse on one side of the rivermouth and an anti-Napoleonic fort and a golf course on the other together with various sheds, in one of which I later discovered a jewel of a beam engine complete with Doric columns to hold up the beam. It was formerly used for hauling boats up, but the owners could no longer get insurance for the boiler. Another antique was the tug *Jumna* with paddle-wheels and the words 'Starboard, Larboard' on the engine telegraph. I never saw it in use but I believe it ended its days at Dunkirk.

Although my mother had much sadness in Redhill in the death of my eldest brother Albert she was more at home there than at Littlehampton and enjoyed a much more social life. On one occasion at Redhill we had a garden party with catering by J. P. Lyons Co. But in comparison Littlehampton was bleak and we tended to 'keep ourselves to ourselves'. This was accentuated when my mother got severe arthritis, though she was always a wonderful mother to us. One result was I think that the only person I really got to know well was a little old lady with the tiniest feet I have ever seen. She was half Italian from her mother and half Scottish from her father and, like my brothers and me, was Chilean, by Chilean law. Her maiden name was Rose-Innes and she married Charles Santley, probably the first singer ever to be knighted; but she called herself Mrs Santley, as they had separated before he got his title. They had quarrelled over the education of their son who died at an early age. Santley was a fanatical Roman Catholic but she no longer took it seriously. She told me that if she had to belong to an organised religious group she would make straight for the Church of England because it was so very English, one was allowed to believe anything and provided you behaved as a gentleman (which incidentally all English priests did) no one quarrelled with you. She was full of anecdotes about artists and singers in London before and after her marriage and she was an admirer of William Morris; the walls of her house were covered with his exhausting wallpapers. Like so many women of her generation, she was self-educated and had made a good job of it. Her reason for building a house at

Littlehampton was that country life was not enjoyable in England unless one was 'county' class; but in a seaside town, class distinction was less visible. This was my first glimpse of the British class system; I had always placed myself 100 per cent in the top class! She had a companion, Miss Neal, and her old family nursemaid lived in the house. But I imagine she was lonely. I used to go to tea once a week and she did not use me as a captive audience, but always wanted to hear what I was doing and thinking. She got on swimmingly with 'Don Pedro' (my father); he would pay her elaborate compliments in Spanish such as 'I walked through your lovely garden this morning, but the most beautiful flower of all, for which I was looking, was not there.' This amused and pleased them both.

When I was about 12 years old, I saw an advertisement for a biography of Edison; I wrote for particulars but never had a reply. Instead two volumes in a cardboard slipcase arrived; my father had sent a cheque for them. They were a revelation and I wandered around in a dream. Samuel Smiles was good but rather remote, this was much closer to modern reality. I was in a huge liner crossing the Atlantic Ocean with my latest invention, which financiers in New York urgently needed to foil Jay Gould's efforts to corner the market in phonographs. My invention called the Sonoscript recorded sound electrochemically on paper soaked in potassium iodide and starch made up for me by Mr Smart, the well-known pharmacist of High Street, Littlehampton. The sound was reproduced by a selenium cell, thus obviating all wear and tear. Or else I was battling for three days and nights without rest to solve a crucial trouble in my electric car, which had a unique lazy tong system allowing me to spread wings out on each side by pulling a lever (this was actually Gordon's idea, inspired by the *Boy's Own Paper*). Finally I settled down to design and construct a chain-stitch sewing machine with my Meccano in order to win a prize and set up in business. But by then it was time to go to a boarding school, misnamed a 'public school', which was *de rigeur* for all upper class English boys.

CHAPTER TWO

LANCING

I WENT to Lancing in September 1918 when World War I was nearing its end. It is one of the Woodard Schools founded by the Reverend Nathanial Woodard (1811-91) to give the alleged benefits of 'public school' (in reality private school) education to the sons of Church of England parents unable to pay the fees of existing 'public schools'. Lancing, founded in 1848, was intended for the upper and wealthier middle class and it was hoped it would give financial assistance to those Woodard schools intended for lower middle class parents. In Victorian times the class strata were well defined.

Woodward was suspicious about female education. In 1884 he wrote, 'After all, we all know what women are for and to draw them from these purposes and put them into conflict with men in the universities, the Forum, and the public streets can only have an unchristian ending.' It would have been entertaining to have had his views on coeducation. He was a single minded man and was always referred to at Lancing as 'The Founder': in his voluminous correspondence, preserved in the main at Lancing, there is very little about friends, his children or indeed his wife.

Wanting a tower at the west end of the school chapel at Lancing, Woodard hit upon the idea of appealing to the women of England by suggesting that it would be a lighthouse and have a chapel at the top

> Where a chaplain and other devout persons may in all great and dangerous storms pass their time in prayer for the deliverance of those in peril of shipwreck, or in any case that they may be supported by Divine power to meet their fate in patience and in a saving faith. Let mothers who have sons, and sisters who have brothers at sea think of this.

This bit of nonsense produced £10,000 in no time at all. The unfunny end of the story is that the money was wasted; Woodard apparently never understood that it is essential to take borings (easily done even in Victorian times) of the subsoil before excavating for foundations. Members of the teaching staff were to be semi-monks willing to accept low wages but this attempt to set up an academic sweat shop was unsuccessful and in 1897, six years after the founder's death, prominent Lancing men circulated a memorandum calling for a change in the system. Its academic status was low but in the years just before World War I, it had begun to improve under its new headmaster, Rev. H. T. Bowlby, who appointed a number of outstanding laymen such as J. F. Roxburgh, W. B. Harris, E. Brentsmith and J. H. Cooper.

My first encounter with the headmaster was unfortunate. We were told to go to the chapel after supper where he had carefully set the stage to make a lasting impression on us on our first day at school. The chapel was in semi-darkness except for some candles in tall candelabra at the foot of the choir stalls. It was magnificent and inspiring, no more austere than Chartres (yes, I was told compare it with Chartres). And there between the candelabra was the welcoming handsome face of Rev. H. T. Bowlby floating above a body hidden in a cassock. His speech gradually reached its climax as he expressed his earnest hope that Lancing would someday produce a great saint and that it might be one of us. Good gracious, I thought, is that what he wants and my mouth must have drooped into its familiar grin. He stopped short and said in a menacing way (George Robey equipped with his umbrella could not have done better), 'Well de Bruyne, will you tell us what amuses you?' My horror and shame increased as the boys around me seemed to edge away from the black sheep sitting there right amongst them. I was literally struck dumb and when I say literally I mean (on this occasion) literally. He repeated his question and I said that I could not imagine myself as a saint. The temperature seemed to drop somewhat and he mumbled 'It would not be a bad thing if you could' or something like that.

When I told W. M. Howitt (the school chaplain) next day about these happenings, his only comment, bless him, was that repartee had never been one of the headmaster's strong points. Thanks to Bernard, who had preceded me at Lancing, and was now in the

Royal Field Artillery in France, Howitt was a friend of the family. He was known as the 'Holy Ghost' because his appearance and his singing voice were ethereal; he was one of the few men I have known whose Christianity irradiated his whole self. He used to say, 'I don't mind what beliefs or unbeliefs people have, provided they agree with me about the rightness of Christ.' In contrast Bowlby never moved me, least of all when he preached a sermon based on newspaper 'info' on the holy life of Sir Charles Santley, shortly after his death in 1922.

When I got to the dormitory I found that someone had collected and put 'daddy longlegs' in my bed. It was the last straw in a long, emotional day, which had started with goodbyes to everyone and my Meccano set. A boy named Hale removed the insects and tried to comfort me, and I soon fell asleep. One's bed in a dormitory was the only place where one could be warm, peaceful, and shut-off from the pandemonium of life in Lower School at Lancing. But though it might be said that Lancing was more brutal than Borstal,[7] it was no more brutal than other public schools. Patrick Summers, who was at Eton from 1954-9 and became President of Techne, Inc. (Princetown, New Jersey), told me that he used to listen as he lay in his bed in his study for the prefect's footsteps which would stop at one of the studies to get the occupant out of bed for caning.

I was undoubtedly a misfit. This is supported by the picture given by Robert Lea,

> Without doubt the most miserable sight I have ever seen in my life was dB as I first remember him. Clothed in shorts and shirt, he was playing football at Lancing. A cold east wind swept the field, but while others rushed energetically up and down dB stood for one and a half hours absolutely stationary in the middle of the field, blue with cold, but always politely facing the direction of the ball. He never altered this method of playing during his career as a footballer.[8]

My football career was mercifully short since as a last resort the house captain responsible for games made me go for cross-country runs. One of my difficulties with soccer was that I never took the trouble to understand the rules; when I tried to get into the opponent's territory there were always rude shouts of 'off side'.

7. Brendan Behan, *Borstal Boy*, London 1958.

8. Extract from a speech by R. F. G. Lea on the occasion of my retirement from CIBA (ARL) Ltd, 6 December 1960.

But cricket was even more boring because whole Saturday afternoons were wasted, as far as I was concerned, watching the school cricket XI. When I had to bat (in junior games) it soon became known that I could be relied upon to hit the ball in a gentle curve straight into the hands of one or other of the fielders called in by the captain to surround me. On one such occasion the Rev. Bowlby was heard to cry 'de Bruyne didn't even try'. Fortunately, rescue eventually came from an unexpected quarter, and not only rescue but a modicum of honour and glory in the form of my school colours. I was appointed spare man to the school shooting team which eventually won the Ashburton Shield at Bisley in 1922. I had discovered that correcting an OTC rifle for distance and wind was not much more difficult than say setting up a reflecting galvanometer.

My next confrontation with the headmaster was over the rite of confirmation. E. B. Gordon was then the effective housemaster of my house (called Head's House because theoretically the headmaster himself was the housemaster and parents were made to pay an extra ten pounds a term for this extra attention). He was a kind and humorous man who called me 'The Ionic Valve' because he saw me reading a book by that name while standing in row for one of the daily roll calls. To the end of his life he sent to all his former pupils at Christmas an extract from the writings of some English mystic beautifully printed on his own printing press. He reported to Bowlby that he did not think I was in the right frame of mind for confirmation. The headmaster sent for me and told me that all his prefects were confirmed. Mallowan, who was a year or so senior to me at Head's House, writes in *Mallowan's Memoirs*:[9]

> When the time came for confirmation I refused, and this deviation from the norm was inexplicable to the closed mind of my headmaster. He warned me that if I persisted in this attitude I could expect no promotion and no authority in the school. I therefore set about persuading my Father, who incidentally was an agnostic, that as far as scholarship was concerned I was wasting my time and would do better to go to the University immediately without divulging to him the real reason for my wish to leave. I had little difficulty in persuading him ....,

9. Sir Max Mallowan, *Mallowan's Memoirs*, London 1977.

Mallowan was an exceptionally intelligent boy and had reached the sixth form when 16 years old; he left Lancing just after his seventeenth birthday. His poor initial performance in his undergraduate days at Oxford may well have been the result of Bowlby's bigotry.

Alas, I was far from being brilliant and so with difficulty suppressing my fury at Bowlby's threat to my career in Lancing I took my dose in the following year of Christian Mythology, silently repeating to myself, 'Eppur si muove' or words to that effect and reminding myself that another Dutchman (Erasmus) had said, 'Let others be martyrs, for myself I am not worthy of that Honour.' But then emotion would overtake me and inspired by H. G. Wells I would say to myself, 'To hell with these priests and their pseudo miracles and bloody sacrifices at the high altar and their mysteries. They are always talking about the great mysteries of life; scientists talk about problems.' The headmaster wrote in my last report how deeply moved he was that 'my earlier difficulties had given way to a steadfast search for truth...' As my fellow citizens in the USA might say, 'Aw shucks!'

I remember with gratitude E. B. Gordon, W. B. Harris and above all J. H. Cooper, the science master, whose parents had unfortunately christened him 'Jabez'. He had graduated at Oxford in chemistry; he was a mountaineer, had seen service in the army for almost the whole of the war and supported his widowed sister and her child in Shoreham. I cannot include J. F. Roxburgh because apart from his readings of French poetry I did not attend his classes. But added to the boredom of games was the dreariness, at least in the Lower School, of uninspired teaching. For instance in my first term I was taught Latin by Mr Smythe, housemaster of Old's House, a disciplinarian who had the ability and apparently the need to stand on one leg when watching football matches. I was given a well-worn book called *Aeneas* and told to translate a passage in which Dido shows her annoyance with the hero. There was no suggestion that the Latin text had a rhythm. There was no information about the author and how his work had been preserved for two thousand years; the only things that Mr Smythe handed out were punishments of various kinds. His attitude was an inevitable reaction to the hostility of the boys – a vicious circle indeed. And of course, in the whole of one's time at Lancing there was no respite from the greatest weariness of all – the hours and hours of compulsory chapel attendance inflicted on us, at least in part by the fanaticism of the governing body. One of the governors wrote without Bowlby's knowledge to all the parents to ask if they thought Lancing had failed in its religious aspects. My mother sent the letter to Howitt, who showed it to Bowlby who cried, 'It's damnable' over and over again. Perhaps it was this kind of pressure on him that made him penalise unconfirmed boys. I eventually found some relief in chapel by getting hold of an American book on electricity bound in limp black covers with red-edged pages looking externally exactly like a bible and I kept it with my hymn book in my stall.

For the first two years or so I lived in constant fear of being caned for quite petty offences, such as being late three times for roll call, or for offences for which I was not directly responsible. If a master made me stay behind at the end of the lesson, I obviously could not carry out my 'fagging' such as tidying up the House common room. After I had left Lancing I had a recurring dream that I was going back, as a new boy, and I would awake and thankfully realise there was no need to worry. Noel Annan[10] discussing public school religion pointed out that:

> The Christian morality that was preached in Chapel roots its tone from the Old Testament. A misdemeanour was a sin; what better remedy than to cane the child and often? sin made the tribe unclean; what better propitiation of Jehovah than to exact mass punishment?

Sanitation and hygiene were primitive. The whole school used centralised WCs, called 'The Groves' which consisted of doorless roofed cubicles in two rows, each with its seat over a common horizontal trough, along which water periodically flushed out onto the sloping ground on the north side of the College buildings. 'The Groves' were open to the skies, they needed to be; there was no provision for washing one's hands. One afternoon when I happened to be there the headmaster himself came out to make an inspection and remarked, 'I can see nothing wrong' – a remark on a par with that of the don at Cambridge who queried the wisdom of installing baths when the undergraduates were only up for eight weeks at a time. Quintin Riley made a special seat in the carpentry workshop for himself which he took daily to the Groves until it was confiscated. After games we were allowed a dip in a hot bath that served for six or seven of us. Hot water was usually short for our regular

10. Noel Annan, *Roxburgh of Stowe*, London 1965.

weekly bath and one frequently had to use the previous bather's water. The authorities had evidently not yet heard of the economy and hygiene of showers.

J. F. Roxburgh was the star turn in the comedy of life at Lancing. Wit, affluence and generosity, charm, impeccable clothes, enthusiasm, knowledge and love of the classics and French poetry, were added to a real and deep interest in his pupils. Others with more experience of him and better literary abilities than mine have written fully and fairly about J. F. Roxburgh and if it be asked how I dare to find fault with such an undeniably great man, I would reply that in my opinion all the Arnolds, Bowlbys, Roxburghs, Woodards, etc., must bear a responsibility for the decline of their country. Their aim was to turn out pupils, as perfectly suitable as they could make them, to run an eighteenth-century world. If I meet them again I will confront them with this charge and they will no doubt rebut it in three ways: (1) they gave what the people asked for (2) the trained minds they produced enabled their pupils to master any subject with ease and (3) science was too narrow and specialised a subject to become the cornerstone of an education for life.

One can soon dispose of (1) by noting that the claim can be even better made by prostitutes; also it is the duty of leaders to lead. But (2) and (3) are more troublesome. As for (2) the trained mind:

> Over the last fifty years and more, careful experiments have been made, with tests before and after training, with control groups etc. One of the earliest was a personal trial by the psychologist, William James. He measured his speed in learning French verse. Then he switched to learning English verse and practised techniques for several weeks. Then, back to French verse: no improvement, no gain from the English practice. Other early results were equally discouraging, almost no transfer. True, students who had done brilliantly at Latin were very clever in other studies. But classics had not necessarily trained their minds or polished their wits – they had always been exceptionally able. Their teachers, who claimed great benefits, should have been more careful to distinguish between *propter hoc* and *post hoc*, between ability because of this, (study of classics) and ability observed there.[11]

11. See Noel Annan, *Roxburgh of Stowe*, London 1965; Eric M. Rogers, *Physics for the Inquiring Mind*, Princeton and London 1960.

However, fuller investigations have shown that transfer does occur though not nearly so easily as had been (and still is) hoped: and only in certain special circumstances which are common ground between the training and the other field strong intellectual feeling, delight, enjoyment, admiration, ambition to make use of the training can all promote some transfer (boredom and dislike have the opposite effect: insulation!).

But, even allowing for transfer in these special examples, I think one is entitled to ask whether a pupil would not become a better scientist if he had spent all his time learning science rather than spending some of his time 'training his mind' in classics first. When I expressed my regret at the time wasted at Lancing in teaching me some Latin, Eric Rogers replied that he himself was glad to have learned Latin as he hoped shortly to get time to read the works of Copernicus as originally published! That is certainly a good though rather an esoteric reason.

As for (3) soon after World War I ended there was considerable popular interest in Einstein's theories of relativity and articles appeared in the type of periodical (such as the *Spectator*) read by J. F. Roxburgh. He probably concluded that his trained mind should enable him to understand relativity; after all he had at least a nodding acquaintance with Kant's views of the universe, why not therefore with Einstein's? Anyway, it is a fact that he gave the classical side of the sixth form a lecture on relativity. Only heaven now knows what he said. It never occurred to him that relativity was a part of physics which is a small section of science, which is the intellectual glory of our age.

In an article in the *New Scientist* in 1958, I wrote:

> In 1914 British industry was based on free trade, an Empire perpetually in the sun and massive investments in other countries; to some extent it may also have been influenced by the preference among gifted men and women of this country for classical education and for a lifetime spent in the service of the Crown or Mammon rather than in making things in dark satanic Mills[12]

I was interested to get support for my conjecture from Professor Gowing's lecture which concludes:

12. N. A. de Bruyne, 'The Future of the D.S.I.R.', *New Scientist* 15 May 1958, pp. 28–9.

> Moving back from atomic energy to the Samuelson and Devonshire papers, I cannot believe there is no connection between them: the smell of Britain's relative decline rises from those pages. Britain had achieved so much in the early nineteenth century with so little education that she had felt no need to create the educational infrastructure which her potential competitors were building in advance of their industrialisation. Despite weighty evidence on the need for scientific and technical education, the infrastructure had not been created in Britain when the century ended. And so the management of British industry until after the Second World War, allowing for the time lag of the human life span, was nurtured in a tradition where such education counted for little. Technical change flowed neither in the blood of the entrepreneurs nor the workers. The divorce of the upper and middle class from science and even from technology set a norm for those who climbed the social ladder behind them.
>
> Hindsight is sometimes called the most reliable form of prophecy. But the prophecies of the 1870s about scientific and technical education were sober foresight. Some historians are determinist, concluding that prevailing doctrines justify, as well as explain, subsequent events. But as one modern German historian has said, 'The historian should restore to the past the freedom of choice it once had. How true this is of the subject of this lecture.'[13]

Lancing, founded in 1848, had to wait sixty years before it got anything resembling a science building.

> The carpentry shop and the matron's quarters between the two new houses connect up with the red brick and tile hung science building erected under the then Custos, Mr William Woodard. This building is an unfortunate blot upon the College, but it must be remembered that it grew from a one-story shed, was added to and finally clothed in its present skin to preserve it until such time as a building worthy of its surroundings can take its place.,[14]
>
> That the natural knowledge which has been given to the world in such abundance during the last fifty years should remain untouched, and that no sufficient attempt should be made to convey it to the young mind growing up and obtaining its first views of those things, is to me a matter so strange that I find it difficult to understand. Though I think I see the opposition breaking away, it is yet a very hard one to overcome. That it ought to be overcome I have not the least doubt in the world.' Lord Clarendon asked him: 'You think it is

13. Margaret Gowing, 'Science, Technology and Education: England in 1870', the Wilkins Lecture 1976, *Notes and Records of the Royal Society,* Vol. 32 (1977–8), pp. 71–90.
14. Maxwell Ayrton, *The College Buildings Since 1910.*

1. Family – 1911
Left to right: Albert, Norman, Father, Gordon, Mother, Bernard

2. Norman de Bruyne, 1941.

3. James Clark Maxwell.

4. The 'Snark', built 1934–5.

N.P. 112.
B.B 735.

NATIONAL PROVINCIAL BANK LIMITED.

17 APR 1936 19

CREDIT the Current Account of

Aero Research

NATIONAL PROVINCIAL BANK LIMITED
11 APR 1936
CAMBRIDGE

£5, £10, etc., Notes			
£1 Notes			
10/- do.			
Gold			
Silver			
Copper			
Postal Orders			
Cheques (as per back)	1000	·	
TOTAL £	1000	-	·

Paid in by de Havilland

5. The cheque for £1,000 from de Havilland, 1936.

now knocking at the door, and there is a prospect of the door being opened?' 'Yes' answered Faraday, 'and it will make its way, or we shall be behind other nations in our mode of education.[15]

Nathaniel Woodard, preferred to stay behind. Mr Giffard, examining Lancing for the Schools Commission, reported that: 'The staple of education is Latin and Greek. The Mathematics receive a moderate degree of attention; French scarcely any; no instruction is given in the physical science; instrumental music, German and drawing are extras.'

The headmaster pressed Woodard in 1869 on the subject of natural science: 'but it was not until 1872 that regular instruction under a qualified teacher was offered at Lancing.' However, no natural science was taught at all at the lower middle class school established at Shoreham in 1858, until after Woodard's death.

Looking at the training of engineers in France and Germany (at the time of Gowing's Lecture) it seemed that there was more of a sense of elitism than in Britain, starting at school. So it appeared that one hundred years had passed and Britain had still not recovered from the damage inflicted on its educational system by eminent Victorian schoolmasters and their descendants.

Surely the evil that men do lives after them.

EMINENT COLLEAGUES

Sir Max Mallowan states in his memoirs:

> Among my contemporaries in a relatively small school of three hundred boys we may count besides Evelyn Waugh, Roger Fulford, later famous for his work on the four Georges; Hugh Molson, later Lord Molson, a pillar of public life, and Humphrey Trevelyan, later Lord Trevelyan, a diplomat who has also enjoyed distinguished careers in many other fields.[16]

To the above, I would add 'Gino' Watkins, explorer who lost his life whilst canoeing at an early age demonstrating turning-over; Driberg who became a prominent left-wing politician; Quill, the

15. Public Schools Commission, 18 November 1862, quoted in J. H. Gladstone, *Michael Faraday*, London
16. Sir Max Mallowan, *Mallowan's Memoirs*, London 1977.

test pilot; and of course, Sir Max Mallowan himself. I spent three weeks having chicken pox with Fulford in the school sanatorium; I got to know Trevelyan at Cambridge, and Watkins was at Head's House when I was head of the house. I first appreciated the quality of Molson's mind when standing next to him compulsorily watching a football match. He spoke not a word to me but treated his companion to a masterly dissertation on the English prison system in answer to the question, 'Do we send people to prison for punishment or reform?' On another occasion we were both in the same divinity class (I don't know how I achieved this) taken by W. M. Howitt whom he reduced to a state bordering on despair by his cross-examination culminating in the question, 'How can the crucifixion bring comfort to the sick, the dying, the bereaved?'

Waugh is the person most people ask me about. He brought fun and excitement into our lives by turning the system upside down and exposing its absurdities. I find that I have acquired from him a 'double take' or 'throwaway line' in conversation; for example, what appears to be a rhetorical question, such as, 'All Lancing men are good fellows, aren't they?' His wit was feared; J. J. Astor told me of the devastating remark Waugh made in later life about one of his friends, who was notoriously not handsome – 'He is not as nice as he looks'.

The OTC, which was under the direction of a militant priest the Rev. Bond, received Waugh's particular attention, and the general reaction after the war helped him. I personally had found a way out of the absurdity of having to move about like a ballet dancer with stiff joints, under the orders of an older boy bawling out his commands at me, by joining the signals section with Robert Lea. The signals were a band of independents looked after by W. B. Harris and one benefit was that I learned the Morse Code, which I shall find useful when I have a stroke.

Waugh looked like a pink fawn. He got great pleasure in carrying out the duties of a minor sacristan and used to chide me for my inability to appreciate the histrionics; but I would not describe him as a really religious person.

He was certainly not a positive influence for good. There is however one side to his character that impressed me and that was his ability to work hard. I had never seen anyone work with his intensity when he realised that his only hope was to get into Oxford. More's the pity that he threw away his opportunities when he got there.

In his last year he abandoned all his friends and accepted the substantial bribe from his housemaster of rapid promotion over them to the position of house captain. He wrote a brilliant play, which was an 'Apologia pro vita sua' and which was performed before the whole school.

MY LAST YEAR

My life at Lancing was transformed in my last year when I got into the upper sixth and became head of the house. I was on my way at last. I felt like 'A Connecticut Yankee at King Arthur's Court' able to leave Merlin mumbling over an altar at one end of Lancing while I had the run of the labs at the other. I liked the responsibility and I scored a victory over the trained minds of the classical sixth by winning the school essay prize. J. F.. Roxburgh had gone on to be headmaster at Stowe and had been succeeded by C. H. Pearson who brought a breath of fresh air into my life and told me I was suffering from religious persecution and who wrote, in my last report (which I found among my mother's papers after her death)

> His spelling is eccentric; he uses too many epigrams; and he has not yet acquired the power of consecutive argument.[17] But all that he writes is well worth reading and he has great literary gifts as well as an intense enthusiasm for his ideas. At the University, if he is properly directed and does not let his humour or his originality run away with him, he will show a first-class intellect.

He told me that Bowlby had asked to see my essay but he had prevaricated successfully and he thought Bowlby would not ask again. As far as I can remember, the theme of the essay was that mankind had reached a stage where science and technology had given hope of a decent life to millions and had made nonsense of the superstitions still being taught at Lancing. That the pursuit of science had advanced basic knowledge of the universe beyond anything man

17. Waugh made a similar criticism of me: 'The motion was "This House considers that the day of institutional religion is over". The debate was wretched. De Bruyne was very scientific but could not arrange his ideas at all. Preters was blasphemous, he did not offend me but I think I was alone in this. J.F. was crushing and prolix; everyone else irrelevant.' M. Davie (ed.), *The Diaries of Evelyn Waugh*, London 1976, p. 143.

My trouble, I think, is due to the fact that my ideas are not the product of consecutive argument. But I test them, preferably in a laboratory. Such people are classified as 'Puzzlers' by Hayek (*Encounter*, Vol. 45, September 1976) and 'Hunters' by Sir Lawrence Bragg (*Proceedings of the Royal Institution*, Vol/42 (1969), p. 405.

had dreamed possible and that education should be primarily based on a search for truth by the methods of science.

No doubt it was crude and immature, yet I would still defend its thesis that events had overtaken the kind of education which Lancing offered. To relegate the teaching of science to slum quarters at the base of the Acropolis and to encourage all the more intelligent boys to study classics, to compel everyone to study 'Divinity' (even in their last year at school) and to spend hours of precious time in a chapel (no matter how beautiful) was a poor kind of introduction to the world they would ultimately meet.

SOME GOOD THINGS AT LANCING

Firstly, one of the events which made life enjoyable was Brent Smith's organ recitals on Sunday evenings. He played 'popular' works of classical music by Beethoven, Schumann, Tchaikovsky and so on. On one occasion, Howitt played the piano part in Beethoven's Emperor Concerto. All this 'orchestral-organ' music was new to me because at the time broadcasting had hardly begun, tapes were unknown, gramophones were crudities and I had never been to a concert of classical music. Nowadays it would probably be thought to be unexciting. But the only other music we heard was 'liturgical music' (hymns and chants) which has the same relation to real music as theological literature has to real literature. Brent Smith would cunningly sometimes play a Bach fugue as we waited our turn to leave at the end of a service. At first I thought them dreary because I was unable to follow the complexity of their structure. Now I bless him for the priceless gift he gave to us. Surprisingly there was no amateur string quartet among the teaching staff I never heard Bowlby or J. F. Roxburgh express any interest in music and until the arrival of G. L. Troutbeck it seemed that only Brent Smith and Howitt had any musical ability among the masters.

Secondly, physical training and running undoubtedly did me a lot of good. Thirdly, some of the masters were exceptionally fine characters and teachers. Fourthly, the environment is superb – better than Harrow's famous hill because the view is not of Wembley but of the sea and the river and downland. It has been unfortunately restricted by a vain glorious extension for which Bowlby's successor must be held responsible.

Lastly, it was the place that one grew up in, where one made friends, it was a community, one learned to endure its unpleasant features; although one knew that there was no one to run to if in trouble, that hard fact was not without value.

EPILOGUE

I left Lancing at the end of July 1923; thirty-four years later Mr Dancy the Headmaster invited me to speak to the school on the occasion of the opening of the 'Advanced Science Laboratories' on 21 September 1957, and this is the substance of what I said:

Speech at the Opening of the Advanced Science Laboratories Lancing College, 21 September 1957

Introduction

There is such a shortage of scientists today, and of money for the endowment of public schools, that certain industrial firms have formed 'The Industrial Fund for the Advancement of Science in Schools' to enable 'unnationalised' schools to bring their science laboratories up-to-date. The action of these firms far exceeds the enlightened self-interest one might reasonably expect of them; I think it is an action of far-seeing statesmanship.

This is a happy day though to you that may sound an odd description on the first day at school after the summer holidays.

But the opening of the additional science laboratories is a happy event in more ways than one. It will make all old Lancing boys happy to know that under the guidance of Mr Dancy the school is looking forward as well as backwards. It makes me happy to know that those of you who want to, will be better able to learn the rules of what is one of the most rewarding games imaginable and one that will last a man all of his life time.

Science as a career

This shortage of scientists is of course a grand thing for us scientists. We have always enjoyed our work and now we are being well paid for it too. But 'don't get me wrong' – I am not suggesting that anyone should become a scientist for the money even though it is true (as Gertrude Stein remarked) that money in one's pocket gives one a warm feeling in one's heart. To do a job for the money only inevitably leads to disaster – I have seen it happen; outraged human nature will exact in happiness all that you may acquire in wealth. You must enjoy your job and in science one can find an interest to suit almost any temperament.

The maths bogey

Now let me say a few words about one of the commonest reasons people give for not taking up with science as a career. It is 'I'm no good at maths.' I'm no good at maths and if you asked me to differentiate logx I would have to ask Mr Kermode for the answer. This is nothing to be proud about of course. But it is true that even in an exact science like physics you can get on with quite a modest equipment of mathematical tools. Indeed I believe you can get to the top because I rather doubt whether my former boss, Lord Rutherford, could have differentiated logx without clearing his throat a bit first.

But again don't get me wrong about this; excuse me if I again give a personal example. Mr Cooper who was head of science at Lancing once said to me, 'de Bruyne you must get a working knowledge of maths if you are going to be a scientist,' and I replied with youthful insolence, in the words of Edison, 'Sir, when I need a mathematician I hire one.' Of course, Mr Cooper was right; but so was I and in this sense – it is not important to be able to turn the handle of the mathematical machine. It is certainly an advantage if you know the tricks of the mathematician's trade, and can manipulate symbols to show unexpected relations between them. But what is *essential* is that you should be able to think out and write down all the facts in a way that will enable a mathematician to deal with them either directly or via one of these modern electronic computers. You should be able to write down the equations but you need not be too worried if you can't solve them. Many years later I had the great privilege of working closely with the chief engineer of the de Havilland Aircraft Company, Mr C. C. Walker, and was delighted to hear him say that he had not yet met a problem which if soluble he could not master in principle with the aid of a piece of squared paper. Don't think that I don't wish I knew more maths than I do. Learn all the maths you can but remember that for a scientist it is a means to an end just like chromatography or glass blowing. Of course to those of you who are pure mathematicians, mathematics is something quite different, it is a creative activity of the highest intellectual kind far removed from the sets of rules which the word signifies for most non-mathematicians.

Learning science

Now having I hope disposed of the maths bogey let me return to science as a career. I said it's not for the money but for the joy that I recommend you take up science. 'Science' of course includes engineering and applied science.

Now you may ask what fun is there in this stuff we learn at school? And I have to admit you have got something there because unfortunately in any subject learning the rules can be rather dull work whether it is scales on the piano or irregular verbs in a foreign language, though the process is enormously helped by the regularity and discipline of life at a boarding school.

Up to 21 or so most of us are at the receiving end of a deluge of instructions, demonstrations and words; then one find's oneself having to do the talking and one feels a considerable sympathy for one's former teachers. From experience of lecturing I can assure you that it chills one to the bone to see a yawn, what one longs to see, as Sir Lawrence Bragg has remarked, is that half grin of interest which says so clearly, 'I see what you're driving at.' So please go half way to meet the men who are teaching you and magically your interest will grow.

We get a wrong impression of science from text books; it all seems so orderly and logical and you can't help contrasting it with the goofy, inconsequent way in which one's own mind works and you can't help concluding that you will never be able to produce this sort of stuff yourself. Quite right; you won't; and no one ever has originated anything in that way.

'Fabian of Scotland Yard' on the TV gives a much better idea of the methods of science than one can infer from say Loney's *Statics and Dynamics.* False trails, misleading evidence, hunches, an idea and finally the test of the theory – those are the map of science in real life.

Let me enlarge on this. In Loney you will find Newton's three laws of motion and then a logical build-up to $s = ut + {}^1/_2\, ft^2$ and so on and all those problems about running up hills and things being shot out of guns and so on. Now this is how it really happened: Somewhere about 1665, shortly after Isaac Newton had taken his degree, when in his own phrase he was in the prime of his age of invention, he had a magnificent poetical idea: if gravity extended to the highest hills, why should it not extend further? Now a scientist has always to remember that beauty is truth and truth beauty. In other words, he can't kid himself and get away with it, and when Newton computed the consequences of his idea on the interaction between the earth and the moon, alas he got no agreement. It was not until 1679, (fourteen years later) that a corrected value for the radius of the earth showed that his idea was truly beautiful because it was true. But he published nothing and not until 1684 at Halley's instigation did he produce the holograph manuscript which is in the Cambridge University Library and which is the basis of his communication to the Royal Society (see *Cambridge Papers* by W. W. Rouse Ball, Macmillan, London, 1918). From this he proceeded to his *Principia* bringing the whole of the solar system to law and order and, in so doing, freeing mankind from the fears of an irrational universe. Those few pages in a text book represent the groping and the struggles, the defeats and triumphs of a genius. The three laws did not spring ready made from Newton's pen, anymore than Beethoven thought up the Fifth Symphony in one coherent effort.

So don't be disheartened by the formality and rigour of the text books and don't be ashamed to ask questions because they might be silly. I have to take many people around our works and am often struck by the fact that the 'big' men are often able to pull me up short by asking questions that a less able man would feel ashamed to ask.

There is another way too to make school work interesting – forgive me if I again draw on my own experience. We all of us have day dreams in which we do wonderful things; one such, which is apparently quite common, is the ability to float gracefully down long flights of steps such as those turret stairs in which Lancing abounds. But we also have more practical day dreams about what we will do in the holidays or when we are grown men.

Now don't neglect those day dreams; they can be helpful to you. My day dream was a lightweight accumulator which would make possible a high speed long range electric car, absolutely silent, gearless, and luxurious.

This idea did much to enliven the duller moments of school life and it soon led me to list the metals one could use and from there to look up compounds that would be insoluble in conducting liquids and so on and hey presto before I knew it I had a framework of inorganic chemistry. I never got that car but I got something very valuable, so take your day dreams seriously they can infuse magic into your work. Another thing I learned later at Cambridge, is that it's best to do the examples first at the end of the chapter and then turn back to the more general formal presentation of the subject; it's the natural way; it's how scientists work.

Enjoying science

Creative work is the work we all want to do. As H. G. Wells remarked, if you look out of the train at back gardens you will see windmills, dove cots, ponds and concrete gnomes made at weekends by papas who probably have a dull job in an office, and it is the weekend that makes their life because then they get an opportunity to create. Scientists like artists have that opportunity all the time and unlike the artists their work has a ready sale. It need not be in research proper, it may be in a factory devising a better way of doing a job or a neater way of making an analysis but whatever a scientist is doing he has an opportunity to express himself. This is a scientific age based on scientific industry and the opportunities for a scientist are legion at all levels.

The highest satisfaction is probably in creative research work where one learns that in losing oneself one finds oneself. You come to look on the nights as the nuisance hours, the hours of waiting.

You will be driven by a force that you did not know you possessed. As Clark Maxwell said, 'What is done by what is called myself is, I feel, done by something greater than myself in me.' Once you have ever experienced *that* you don't mind what, to other people, looks like plain drudgery. No one need waste a tear for Madame Curie shifting a ton of pitchblende to get less than a peppercorn of radium or for Whittle battling with an intractable turbine running at speeds that made the hair of turbine engineers stand on end. At those times they were happy in a way that comes to grow people. Not many of us can be Cockcrofts or Langmuirs or a Walton but as I have already said one can get out of science a satisfaction commensurate with your ability at any level.

Arts man and science man

Because the new science block is I understand specifically for advanced teaching I have been stressing science as a career but of course the world needs artists and musicians and writers too. These are activities as important to a full life and the survival of our civilisation as those of the scientist. But there are two points to bear in mind. Firstly that we are short of scientists and we must have more if we are to maintain our economic position without which we cannot rise above poverty and, secondly, that whatever your job or profession may be, you will be immersed in a fundamentally technological civilisation. 'It no longer ceases to be a joke' as the phrase goes, when a man finds himself at the mercy of ideas and forces he cannot understand and is required to give decisions on reports full of words and ideas that are quite new to him.

In this respect there has been a considerable change in attitude. Forty years ago the general view at Lancing was that men on the classical side had broader minds and wider vision than those on the modern side and that the trained mind of the classical scholar enabled him to range over the whole of human knowledge and to jump chamois-like from peak to peak, leaving the narrow scientific specialists stumbling in the valley mud below. We scientists were banished to the western edge of Athens and given a building built in the West-Worthing-Flamboyant style whose upper storey housed rows of pianos from which the felt had long since gone.

Imagine our joy and satisfaction when that lovable classical master, J. F. Roxburgh one day realized that there was a thing called

Relativity and without further ado gave an exposition of it to the classical Sixth Form.

Now the pendulum seems to have swung the other way and Cambridge is thinking of introducing a year's general science in the work for the Arts degree Tripos. It has already introduced lectures on the history of science for those taking the Natural Sciences Tripos.

In my opinion the belief that scientists tend to be narrow specialists has no factual basis. Whether a man is narrow in outlook depends much more on his character than on what he learns at school. A man can be narrow-minded in any activity humanistic or scientific. It might even be said for example that that distinguished poet and classical scholar, Housman, was a narrow man because a good half of human culture and life was a closed book to him; judged by such standards he was indeed a pathetic figure.

Conclusion

My theme has been 'Enjoy your work.' If you can join enthusiasm with knowledge, and a cool head with a warm heart, then Lancing will have cause to be proud of you.

That is true whether you take up science or anything else but if you do take up science this new laboratory can help you tremendously; make the most of it!

As an old Lancing boy may I invoke the privilege of a member of the family of being frank without loss of affection and say bluntly that while this is a good beginning it is only a beginning? Unless Lancing extends and improves its scientific instruction irresistible economic forces will erode it away. Soon there will be few jobs for those without some knowledge of science. We betray the trust in us of the young if we send them out ill-equipped for the battlefield of life as it will be in say ten years' time. The public schools have always rightly placed emphasis on character but character that is not wedded to knowledge is unfruitful.

And finally a word to the master. What a tremendous responsibility you have beneath the petty routine of each day's work! We in industry are depending on you; this laboratory is a symbol of the significance that industry sees in your job. May it be an inspiration to you and may I give you my heartfelt best wishes for the success of your important work.

CHAPTER THREE

WEMBLEY

AFTER leaving Lancing at the end of July 1923, I heard the good news that I had passed my higher certificate in physics, chemistry, maths and (of course!) divinity, with distinction in chemistry – thanks to Jabez Cooper. This excused me from entrance exams to get into the University of Cambridge. I also had to decide how to use my time. The conventional answer was that I should become a temporary tutor to a family who needed to take certificates (A or O) and on talking to my wise old friend, Mrs Santley, she expressed horror and said that will never do and she asked me, 'What was that new research lab about which I was talking to her recently which had just been opened by the British General Electric Company and why did I not get in touch with them?' Accordingly I got my father to write to the relevant director and we eventually made a trip to Wembley and were greeted by a rather rough individual who suggested a token salary of ten shillings a week to assist Mr Dudding in charge of a Lummer-Brodhun photometer. Everything and everybody was new. The whole place delighted me. My father and I found a bed and breakfast in Wembley. I spent the summer at the research laboratories of the General Electric Company Ltd. (no connection with the GE of USA) by the kindness of the director, Clifford Paterson (later Sir Clifford Paterson FRS 1879-1948) at a nominal wage of ten shillings a week (arithmetically equivalent to fifty 'new pence' but in terms of real money worth a good deal more, though less than my lodging house expenses of thirty shillings a week). I was put in the care of a young man named Wilson who was using a Lummer-Brodhun photometer to measure the spatial distribution of illumination from electric light fixtures under the direction of L.B.W. Jolley, formerly of the GPO research laboratory and whose father had been Mayor of Cambridge.

The organisation was unique and was based on the concept that every research worker should know what was going on. This required a battalion of typists to send out a precis to every member of the staff of any incoming letter that might be of interest. In a similar 'democratic' spirit published papers omitted the names of the authors and substituted a statement that the paper was the work of the research laboratories of the General Electric Company. This practice, however, did not last very long.

To get to work I took the Bakerloo tube to North Wembley and sometimes Paterson and his chief confidant, B.P. Dudding, would be on the same train. They were always friendly and approachable but I did not get to know them well of course until many years later. Paterson and his wife spent a night at my home during the last war and gave a talk to the staff of Aero Research Ltd. Paterson always wore suits which seemingly had no buttons, and this was before days of zip fasteners. It may have been because he was a keen yachtsman. In later years Dudding told me that Paterson had a strong temper but had learned to control it. He was an intensely religious Baptist and like Reith of the BBC chose his senior staff to have similar views if possible. The unintended result was to make the labs a Christian enclave in a firm whose founder and boss was Jewish. Dudding had started life as a docker and had come up the hard way; he told me that he was always telling Paterson that his enthusiasm for free masonry was because the Baptists were starved of ceremony and that it would be much less trouble if Paterson changed over to the Church of England! Dudding did an excellent job in introducing quality control based on statistical analysis into the General Electric production plants and a time-and-motion-study man who came to work at Techne (Cambridge) told me that Dudding's visits were always welcomed as he had such a friendly, cheerful outlook. Dudding did not set up a quality control department imbued with a 'holier than thou, do what I say, or else' spirit. He got the workers on the shop floor to plot their own results and as most of the machinery was automatic, there was little temptation to fudge the readings. Dudding's work was done before the introduction (during World War II) of statistical quality control from the USA. Other people I met or worked for at Wembley were Dr C. J. Smithells in charge of metallurgy, Dr Norman R. Campbell (former Fellow of Trinity College, Cambridge). R. W. W. Sanderson in charge of dry battery research and with whom I published my first paper (*Faraday Society* 23 (1927): 'The electrostatic capacity of aluminium and tantalum anode films'). Sanderson told me that Paterson liked manly men and this meant he had to go yachting with him, which was extremely hard work!

I spent three summers at Wembley; the last period was the summer of 1927. I always stayed with an elderly spinster called Miss Dunt and I was perpetually 'ragged' by my Trinity friends, who wanted to know when I was going to make an honest woman of her.

At Wembley I learned a number of useful techniques, not least that of high vacuum research, or what was called a high vacuum in those days (10-6mm Hg.) I also hope I lost a lot of snobbishness as it became obvious that my young colleagues who had never been to a 'public school' had better manners than mine and were more intelligent, knowledgeable and kind-hearted.

Another valuable outcome was an introduction given me by Clifford Paterson to Dr Pirani, director of research of the Osram Company in Berlin. It was the beginning of a lifelong friendship; although a good deal older than me, he had the knack of getting on with younger people. He said you must take risks and be undeterred by sharp and sometimes naive criticism.

Without a doubt my time at Wembley had a powerful formative influence on me, and the techniques I learned there have been invaluable.

CHAPTER FOUR

CAMBRIDGE

I WENT up to Cambridge in October 1923. It was dark when I arrived and I took a taxi to 8 Jesus Lane, which was the lodging house assigned to me by my tutor and which would be my address for my first year. After a while I heard the patter of feet behind the taxi; it was a number of boys following it in the hope of carrying my trunk into the house.

Unlike universities and colleges in USA, the University of Cambridge made no effort in those days to welcome its new customers (and possible future benefactors). No 'meet one another' parties, no addresses of welcome from the Master (however, three cheers for that) no invitation to an inaugural dinner. Nothing. The only thing to do was to go to a (silent) cinema, of which there were six, one for each weekday, or hope that you might meet a similarly lonely schoolmate.

My first contact with authority, apart from a brief handshake with my tutor, F. J. Dykes, was with my director of studies, Tresillian C. Nicholas. We did not know that in seventeen years' time he would introduce me to my future wife, and that although a geologist he would become Senior Bursar of Trinity College and would live to be a 100 years old. A striking, kind face and a Roman nose was what I first saw. He explained that for Part One of the Natural Sciences Tripos one had to select three sciences. Physics and Chemistry were obvious choices; the third choice gradually narrowed down to geology or mineralogy. Though he was scrupulous not to press the claims of his own subject, I sensed that he thought geology was a more valuable study than mineralogy. Nevertheless, I chose mineralogy as I thought that crystallography would be closer to physics than geology. It was a bad choice. Mineralogy was a Victorian vestigial subject carried on by an ancient professor who might well have been a student of William

Hallowes Miller (1801-80) himself. His name was Professor Lewis Vice Master. He had the reputation of being a mine of stale information and someone unkindly remarked that Professor Lewis's grandmother must have been a very well informed woman. He lived in Trinity and I believe had life tenure under the old statutes. His joy was to strike your specimen off one of the single circle goniometers provided for students with a cry of 'That's all wrong.' Our textbook was Dana's *Mineralogy*. X-ray crystallography was scarcely mentioned. The second-in command was Hutchinson who was growing old waiting for Lewis to shuffle off. He was a good teacher and later became Master of Pembroke College. His son, who was a year older than me, became an outstanding ecologist and wrote a charming account of life at Cambridge in *The Kindly Fruits of the Earth* (Yale University Press,1979).

In chemistry we had Fenton who could write on the blackboard with three hands and who as a young man had written a textbook on inorganic analysis which he labelled Volume One. All his life he was badgered by questions about Volume Two. Finally the time came to retire. I attended his last lecture, which was a moving experience. He had arranged a series of 'spectaculars' including a number of explosions and a demonstration of a blood test which he claimed had sent more than one man to the gallows. When later asked about Volume Two he announced that he was devoting the rest of his life to bridge.

Occasionally we heard Sir William Pope, the professor of chemistry who lectured us in a steady monotone as though he were an automaton. If an interruption occurred, he would mentally run the tape backwards and then carry on with the four or five sentences which had preceded the interruption. It was uncanny and one could just as well, in fact better, have read the script oneself. Eric Rideal in a talk given in 1970 on 'Sixty Years of Chemistry' had this to say:

> I found one very great difference between working at Bonn and working at Cambridge. In Cambridge I remember one day being in the laboratory, at the end of which was a long glass passage and I saw a tall lank figure going along there. 'Who's that?' I asked. 'That's your professor, Sir William Jackson Pope, Knight of the British Empire' was the reply. While in Bonn, Anschutz would come around four or five times a week in his top hat and frock coat and say, 'Wie geht's Herr Rideal?' And that made a lasting impression on me; one should not practice apartheid in a laboratory.[18]

The delivery of the Cavendish professor of Physics, Sir Ernest Rutherford, was very different. His enthusiasm was such that it sometimes got out of control as when he stated that 'some of the particles achieved a velocity of 350,000 km/sec.' This led to prolonged gentle stamping and a puzzled look on Rutherford's face. His lectures were frequently illustrated with excellent demonstrations performed by his browbeaten assistant, W. H. Hayles.

J. J. Thomson occasionally gave lectures. He had a habit, rather like President Carter, of relaxing into a kind of smile or grin when he paused and it was rather disconcerting, as it made one think one had missed the point of a joke, but I have been told that it was merely a necessary adjustment of his ill-fitting false teeth. While we always thought of him as the discoverer of the electron, I remember him demonstrating Mayer's experiment in which small magnets in corks float in water under the influence of a vertical electromagnet to illustrate his conception of arrangement of electrons in an atom. He had all the ideas of covalent forces and so on between atoms but he was naturally restricted by the 'laws' of classical physics.

The worst lecturer was C. T. R. Wilson, inventor of the cloud chamber. His class rapidly diminished to one or two faithfuls. But to those patient and intelligent enough to interpret his speech and his handwriting (I was not one of them) it must have been a rewarding task, as Blackett has testified:

> I first met C. T. R Wilson just after World War I when I attended his lectures on light. His voice was not easy to follow, and his blackboard was difficult to read, but somehow I took adequate notes and those are almost the only lecture notes of my days to which I have repeatedly returned. He had a penetrating but very simple approach to wave phenomena in particular to interference and diffraction ...

Lawrence Bragg made a similar comment – 'The very best material presented in the very worst delivery of any lectures I know.'[19]

Practical physics was taught by Searle, who had in his youth met Clark Maxwell. 'He was very kind to me' he said. Searle had also known Oliver Heaviside and told us that Heaviside brewed up enough tea to last a week in order to save the trouble of constantly making it. Searle adopted an air of ferocity and was, I am sorry to

18. 'Sixty Years of Chemistry'. Talk given by Sir Eric Rideal FRS at the official opening of the west wing of the Unilever Research Laboratory, Port Sunlight, 20 July 1970.

19. Lawrence Bragg, 'Reminiscences of Fifty Years', *Proceedings of the Royal Institution*, Vol.41 (1966-7)

say, particularly hard on women students, one of whom it is said was ordered to remove her stays when she was having trouble with a tangent galvanometer (a useless piece of apparatus based on the erroneous belief that the magnetic field in a laboratory is constant). But after I had been around in Cambridge for some years he would jump off his bicycle if he saw me in the street and greet me with a gruff 'You all right?' (pronounced as one word). He would frequently invite students to tea and then forget so that Mrs Searle had to fill the gap. He looked exactly like the professor in Conan Doyle's *The Lost World*. He always referred to Rutherford as 'Professor Radium', the character in a children's comic weekly called *Puck*, which I had read at Littlehampton.

The experiments in his class were usually homemade, unique, and sometimes over-elaborate and irritating as when one was required to measure the surface tension of water by applying a pressure difference computed from a knowledge of the temperature of hot air. The lab was kept in running order by a remarkable young man called 'Tilly' (Clarence G. Tilly; he eventually became a chief assistant and retired about 1966), who could make anything work. It was all very different from what I saw in the 1970s, at Princeton where the students were measuring the velocity of light with Foucault's apparatus. Searle took a keen interest in what was going on in the physiological lab because he disapproved strongly of vivisection. He always emphasised that Kelvin was careful in his definition of the second law of thermodynamics to limit it to inanimate systems; Searle claimed to have seen the wonders of prayer in restoring a sick person to health in defiance of the second law.

When in later years I had to teach elementary physics to engineering students, I thought of all the lectures I had myself attended. The engineering labs at that time seemed not yet to have heard of the invention of printing, because the lecturers lectured by writing on the blackboard almost everything they said and the dutiful but bored audience copied it all down. Although the buildings were relatively new, no provision had been made for a small demonstration room (adjacent to the lecture room) where demonstrations could be got ready while another lecture might be going on. Nevertheless I was determined not to take the easy way out and conform and I believe I was successful. Fairly recently I was manning a stand at the Coliseum, New York, when a man came up and said, 'Sir, are you still lecturing?' I said, 'No, I am now having even more fun.' And he went on, 'What a shame. They were the best lectures we had at the engineering lab.' I could have hugged him. Good lecturing technique can be and should be taught. For self-help start with Michael Faraday's little book, *Advice to a Lecturer*[20] and go on to my late friend, Kitson Clark's *The Art of Lecturing; Some Practical Suggestions.*[21]. But technique is not enough, the lecturer must be responsive to his audience; the lecturer is the servant of his audience. He is there to teach, to help, not to show his own brilliance; after all the audience have paid him, haven't they?

After the above digression I have to record that in the Prelim exam at the end of my first year I got a First, which was unfortunate because it gave me a false sense of achievement and in fact I had largely been living off knowledge acquired in my last year at school. In my second year I got involved in undergraduate journalism, debating at the Magpie & Stump Society, of which I became president, in Trinity, and so on and my Alma Mater administered a sharp slap to my self-esteem when in Part One of the Natural Sciences Tripos taken at the end of my second year I was placed in the second class.

I came up for the Long Vacation and for the first time sat in a hard chair at a clear table with a text book (Poynting & Thomson's *Properties of Matter* to begin with) and worked through it on my own, and found great satisfaction in doing so.

At the end of the long vacation I had made up my mind to take two years before sitting for Part Two (Physics) of the Natural Sciences Tripos examinations.

In the first of those two years in the Part Two Physics, laboratory work was run by Thirkill, who afterwards became Master of Clare College. For the second of the two years Patrick Blackett took over from Thirkill and introduced a number of new experiments made with the simplest of materials. We used ball bearings as spacers and pieces of plate glass to make Fabry Perot interferometers and a Wimshurt machine gave a steady enough voltage to repeat Millikan's determination of the charge on an electron (there were no van de Graafs.) A quartz capillary U tube with mercury and momentarily heated at the bottom of the U made a splendid mercury arc (no one worried about mercury poisoning in those days; the Cavendish must have been saturated anyway from the spillings

20. Michael Faraday, *Advice to a Lecturer*, London 1960.

21. G. S. R. Kitson Clark, *The Art of Lecturing: Some Practical Suggestions*, Cambridge 1957.

of generations of staff and students). Nor did anyone worry about contamination from radioactivity.

My director of studies for Part Two was Charles Ellis, who was an excellent lecturer and teacher and a charming man. He was educated at the RMA Woolwich, had been in the Royal Engineers, and sent to Germany to learn the language; he was interned together with Chadwick and Hatfield, an inventor and consultant, in Ruhleben. There Chadwick taught Ellis radioactivity.

In my second year I had been given rooms at the top of staircase G in Whewell's Court over the rooms of Professor Bevan, elected fellow in 1890, and professor of Arabic since 1893, who according to J. J. Thomson always refused to accept his Trinity fellowship dividend. He was a friendly man and he used to invite undergraduates (living on his staircase) in and give us very hot chocolate to drink. It is said that at meetings to decide on college prizes etc., he would vote for all the candidates so that he could afterwards call on the unsuccessful ones and assure them that he had voted for them. I never dreamed that one day I should have to arrange his funeral. He died in the happiest way; he went out for his afternoon walk, sat down on a bench and was found dead there that same afternoon.

The college rules required me to give up my room at the end of my third year unless I was willing to share a double set. Fortunately I found that Arthur Lister, grandson of Lord Lister, a medical student, who had been at Lancing, was in a similar situation so we decided to take a plunge and got a pleasant room on staircase A in Neville's Court. I took my BA in 1926. The gamble was successful, largely due to Arthur Lister, who brought with him a number of delightful friends. Arthur became an ophthalmic surgeon at Moorfield Hospital. We both worked hard knowing that our futures lay entirely in our own hands. When staying at his home I heard his mother say to him, 'You will have to be the rich one Arthur to support the others' which made him indignant: 'Why pick on me to have to be rich?' Alas, within a few years all three of his brothers were dead.

It was through Arthur Lister and Archibald Prior, who, married one of Arthur's sisters, that I joined the 'Lake Hunt' which was a paper chase held daily for about a week at the end of the summer term in the lake district where a house was rented by a group of Trinity men. Adrian (later Lord Adrian – Master of Trinity) was there on that occasion and it was the first time that I had met him.

In that year there was also a total eclipse of the sun visible from Yorkshire which most of us went to see. So that fixes it as the year 1927.

One thing that struck me was the small number of 'public school' men who read science. Nearly all my colleagues were from grammar schools.

In 1927, I took Part Two of the Natural Sciences Tripos and got a First. This certainly marked the attainment of a peak in my life showing me dazzling possibilities such as research at the Cavendish, a prize fellowship at Trinity, a PhD, becoming a don, and then perhaps an entrepreneur. It was a moment only rivalled by an occasion when flying my homemade Snark aeroplane 6000 feet over the English Channel I saw for the first time the shore lines of England and France stretched out before me in the sunlight.

I spent the summer of 1927 at the research labs of GEC working under B. S. Gosling on 'Field Emission' which is the emission of electrons (even at room temperature) under strong electric fields (ten million volts/cm) from microscopic sharp points on the cathode and which was proving a nuisance in high power transmitting valves. He was a friend of G. P. Thomson (son of J. J. Thomson) from Cambridge days. He was most helpful and when I blundered he would only say, 'You're a young man in a hurry.' Thanks to him I was able to take back with me to the Cavendish Laboratory an all glass mercury diffusion pump with a graded seal, an old glass working machine for sealing in 'pinches' (a pinch is that part of a lamp to which the cap is fixed), a glass vapour trap for immersion in liquid air and miscellaneous equipment. Vacuum technology was still in rather a primitive state at the Cavendish in those days.

CHAPTER FIVE

THE CAVENDISH

THE Cavendish Laboratory was completed in 1874 in the style sometimes known as gas pipe gothic and its construction was personally supervised by James Clark Maxwell (1831-1879), the first professor. His photograph (see Plate 3) was taken when he was a young prize fellow of Trinity College before he grew the beard that make pictures of him look like a mixture of Karl Marx and Jupiter.

The entrance porchway bore the words taken from the Vulgate: 'Magna opera domini exquisita in omnes voluntates eius' – 'The works of the Lord are great; sought out of all those that have pleasure therein' (Psalm III, verse 2, in the English prayer book). Patrick Summers has pointed out to me that the wording in the proposed Book of Common Prayer (USA 1975) is easier to understand – 'great are the deeds of the Lord they are studied by all who delight in them'.

After the death of Maxwell, at the age of 48 in 1879, Lord Rayleigh (1842-1919) was appointed Cavendish professor but went back to his country home in 1884 to continue his research work there. He was followed by J. J. Thomson (1856-1940) who in 1919 was followed by Rutherford (1871-1937). Since then, we have had Lawrence Bragg, Mott, Pippard and Edwards. I would be invidious and impertinent to pick out one of these men as the greatest of them all. I confess that I have always had a warm feeling for Clark Maxwell as a man. His bust has engraved on it 'dp/dt' – a typical Maxwell joke

$$+ dp/dt = JCM$$

(What an extraordinary feat of intuition to endow the 'displacement' current in a capacitor with the same magnetic properties as a current in a conductor and thus to write equations of electromagnetic wave motion in space and to draw the conclusion that the ratio of the capacity of a condenser (capacitor) measured in electromagnetic units to that measured in electrostatic units is (wait for it!) the speed of light!)

Thumbing through his collected works is entrancing. Maxwell's demon was a little fellow who easily upset the second law of thermodynamics; his job was to open a trapdoor whenever he saw a fast molecule approaching but to keep it shut for a slow molecule. In this way he created a difference in temperature without doing work. Although his operations nowadays might be frustrated by the uncertainty principle he remains as a demonstration that our knowledge of atoms is largely statistical and that the ability to create order out of disorder is one of the characteristics of life. The colour top which Maxwell is holding in his hand (see Plate 3) was the first scientific basis of colour analysis; it was a device for mixing reflected colours and he showed that the combination of three primary colours plus a saturation effect accounted for all our sensation of colour. He also made the first colour photographs. His work is the basis of the impressionist and pointillist techniques of painting. Maxwell showed that every material has a relaxation time equal to the ratio of the shear modulus + dp/dt = JCM to its viscosity and that whether we regard a material as a solid or a liquid depends upon the ratio of the relaxation time to our life time. Then there is his work on the kinetic theory of gases and in a quite different sphere his investigation of the control system of Lord Ross's telescope and the introduction of a derivative term to prevent oscillation, and much, much more before he died aged 48. When nauseated by the bogus intellectually exact language of some self-styled social 'scientist' I like to recall Maxwell's definitions of the three ways in which heat can be transmitted:

> Conduction – The flow of heat through an unequally heated body from places of higher to places of lower temperature.
>
> Convection – The motion of the hot body itself carrying its heat with it.
>
> Radiation – In radiation the hotter body loses heat and the colder body receives heat by means of a process occurring in some intervening medium which does not itself thereby become hot.

Can you improve on them?

Lord Rayleigh like Lord Cavendish and le Duc de Broglie, was both an aristocrat and a scientific genius. His research on acoustics and optics is probably of more direct interest to modern technology than Maxwell's. His outstanding gift was to take a thoroughly obscure problem, such as say the resolving power (as distinct from magnifying power) of an optical system, and with penetrating analysis and simple experiments to leave it crystal clear. My friend, Nigel Strutt, who was a fellow part time director of Eastern Electricity, once showed me Lord Rayleigh's laboratory at Terling. Everything was just as he had left it, the equipment was basic and simple.

J. J. Thomson always known to us as 'JJ' was a man of whom I was fortunate enough to see quite a lot. He had from the back a rather Charlie Chaplin look, accentuated by a short walking stick which he waved behind him while he gazed intently into a shop window. His taste in shop windows was catholic and there was much speculation as to whether he was looking at the contents or at infinity. But I believe he was looking at the contents because he once remarked to me that one of the best social changes in his lifetime had been the growth of multiple shops where working girls could get cheap pretty dresses. I thought it was a much better observation than that of the Archbishop of Canterbury who said that the most important invention in his lifetime had been that of the self-wicking candle. J. J. Thomson's name will always be linked with the discovery of the electron, a particle which he found had a mass about 1/2000 of that of a hydrogen atom: it gave him tremendous pleasure when his son later proved that it also behaved like a wave. 'JJ' showed great interest in Aero Research Ltd. He came out to Duxford in 1934 to the official opening when he was 78 years old. I now realise what an effort it must have been to him. I remember him saying, 'I hope de Bruyne that you will make a lot of money because Charles Parsons tells me that to do so is the mark of a good engineer.' 'JJ' had a saint-like character and was universally respected. He had been educated at the then newly opened Owen's College which later became the University of Manchester. Incidentally, in 1877 Nathaniel Woodard refused to support its formation because it did not make religion the foundation of its instruction.

Professor Alexander said, 'It is curious that two of the greatest men of our day were both boys. Einstein was a merry boy until sobered by recent tragedies and Rutherford was a rowdy boy.' Rutherford was very much like a self-made business man in his day-to-day behaviour but he was a genius when engaged in hunting atoms. I left the Cavendish by the time that Lawrence Bragg arrived, but as he was also a fellow of Trinity College I got to know him. He had a gift for explaining physics in a simple fundamental way. When sitting next to him at a concert in the drawing room of the Master's Lodge, during an interval he sketched out on his programmes the double helix which Crick and Watson had just devised. He was excited about it but not yet prepared to give it his full personal authority. He was unique in his empathy with and understanding of industry and came out to Duxford on several occasions. When he later became director of the Royal Institution he asked me to give a Friday night discourse on 'How glue sticks', which I did on 31 May 1957.

In September 1927 I visited USA for the first time to attend the wedding of my eldest brother Bernard to Mary Elizabeth Hayward of Boston. I also managed to squeeze in a visit to the GE laboratories at Schenectady. It was the age of prohibition, without any thoughts of a great depression. It was still the roaring twenties, an age of reaction from a terrible war.

I returned at the end of September 1927 to Cambridge and set up my equipment in the Cavendish Laboratory in a small room on the ground floor with a little day light coming in from Free School Lane. It was at the end of the Cavendish Laboratory which abutted the Department of Collois Science (run by Profesor Eric Rideal) and one had to go through a much bigger room used by T. E. Allibone, E. T. S. Walton and occasionally by J. D. Cockcroft. Allibone had been seconded from the research laboratories of Metropolitan Vickers and had a Tesla transformer which could generate up to 600,000 volts and with endless toil and unfailing cheerfulness constructed vacuum tubes with his own hands which could withstand 450,000 volts in air and 600,000 volts in oil. He obtained intense beams of 1 milliampere electrons through a slit orifice. At that time although only alpha particles had produced disintegrations, there was no known reason why high energy electrons should not also enter nuclei and the Professor (Rutherford) was a firm believer in 'try anything once and see'. Walton arrived at the same time as I did; he came from Trinity College, Dublin, with the idea of accelerating electrons by an ingenious device of his own which became known as the betatron. He was an Ulsterman and when I said I had never heard of the Battle of the Boyne he told me of the visitor who expressing similar ignorance was told 'Go home lad and read your bible!'

Most of Cockcroft's time was occupied in assisting Kapitza, but he appeared intermittently and I believe was interested to see if ions could be diffracted.

Later Cockcroft and Walton joined forces and set up equipment to accelerate protons (positively charged hydrogen ions) with up to 500,000 volts (DC). It seemed rather a hopeless quest until the situation was transformed by a young Russian theoretical physicist called Gamow (1904-68) who predicted that contrary to classical physics there was a finite probability of producing disintegrations at such comparatively low voltages. I recall Cockcroft's pleased expression when he told me of the significance of Gamow's work, and later on Cockcroft and Walton became noted laureates for their successful 'splitting of the atom' which marked the beginning of heavy physics. Gamow had an attractive, whimsical character. He had thrown out a number of letters from the aeroplane on his flight to England and was waiting to hear if any had reached their destination. He later wrote a series of entertaining popular science books after his emigration to USA.

My time at the Cavendish was one of drastic changes in the world of physics, and even the older physicists eventually lost their innocence. As J. B. S. Haldane put it, 'My own suspicion is that the universe is not only queerer than we suppose but queerer than we can support.'

This 'Angst' did not arise from the impact of the theory of relativity, although that had made it clear that common sense can be uncommon nonsense (? Disraeli.) Its impact on atomic physics was negligible and Rutherford's reply to Stephen Leacock, who had asked for his opinion of Einstein's theory, was in the circumstances a correct one – 'Oh, that stuff! We never bother with that in our work.' He also said, 'Don't let me catch anyone talking about the Universe in my department.'

The trouble was that all the immensely successful and comfortable explanations of radio, light and x-rays as wave motions and of the electron as a small negatively charged particle had now to be reconciled with the facts that light could also behave as a particle and an electron could behave like a wave. Logically it was nonsensical, but yet it was true – 'Queerer than we can support.' Eddington playfully called these 'wave-particles' as 'wavicles'.

Perhaps the event that first really shook the physicists were A. H. Compton's photographs in 1923 of the tracks formed in a Wilson cloud chamber showing the collision and recoil of an x-ray with an electron. They could only be explained by assuming that the x-ray behaved as a particle (a photon). In 1905 Einstein had explained the photoelectric effect as a release of electrons from a metal under the impact of photons and Millikan had verified Einstein's equation, and as long ago as 1900, Planck had come to the conclusion that radiation was emitted in packets. But the evidence of the Compton effect was so much more direct that even a horny handed experimental physicist like me could understand it. Cockcroft recalled that the Kapitza Club (an informal postprandial discussion group founded by Kapitza in 1922) at a meeting in 1923 discussed the Compton effect and did not believe it.

Then in 1927, G. P. Thomson (son of JJ) in England and Davison and Germer in USA showed that electrons behaved like the waves predicted by de Broglie if given the opportunity to do so. A characteristic feature of wave motion is the interference that occurs when two wave motions, each of the same frequency and amplitude, are superimposed on each other. If the crest of one motion falls on the crest of the other, the resultant light is increased, if the crest of one falls on a trough of the other, darkness is produced. Thomas Young (1773-1829) and Fresnel (1788-1827) had been able to demonstrate this interference and thus finally caused Newton's particle theory of light to be abandoned.

The theoretical physicists had a field day, much to Rutherford's amusement -'The theoretical men are up on their hind legs again and it is time we shot them down,' he said. But in 1926, Schrodinger 'came up with' a wave equation which restored order without recourse to clockwork and soon after came Heisenberg's principle of indeterminacy (1927) which showed that one cannot simultaneously pinpoint the position and velocity of motion of an electron or photon. The laws of atomic physics index (e.g. air) is reflected back at the interface between the two media instead of passing outward as would be expected. However, we can 'frustrate' this internal reflection if we can bring up an object in the second medium close enough to the interface; it has to be within a wavelength of light.

It is interesting to note that about the same time, Gamow, as already mentioned, used 'tunneling' to explain the ejection of particles from a radioactive nucleus. Fowler told me he was sorry he had not thought of that application.

I saw Nordheim on a number of occasions and I was unfortunately responsible for involving him in an unpleasant incident. I asked him to tea together with a German undergraduate who was at Trinity, through some Anglo-German scholarship. It soon became clear that the undergraduate was a Nazi and/or a violent anti-semite. Some years later I asked Jim Butler about him and he told me that this undergraduate had been reporting back to the German Embassy in London about Cambridge and in particular about Jim Butler himself.

We worked in dire poverty under conditions which no factory inspector would have permitted, under the booming voice of Rutherford, who was eventually persuaded by Cockcroft to install an internal telephone system, which Wynn Williams then connected to the GPO system by some ingenious switchery, but no one ever dared to stop Rutherford from emerging from his office and bellowing for his long-suffering lecture room assistant and secretary W. H. Hayles, whom he had inherited from 'JJ'. Hayles was in advance of his time as he made it his duty to tell everyone that smoking is a dirty habit.

Most of my contemporaries had spent the Long Vacation in 'the nursery' which was the attic, learning the arts and crafts of radioactivity under the mournful eyes of James Chadwick. They were then assigned a research task and more or less left to get on with it.

Rutherford was my official supervisor for my PhD which required three years' research and he used to visit me on Saturday mornings (in those days the whole world worked on Saturday mornings). But I was not one of his boys and he could not have the interest in my work that he otherwise might have had, nor could he advise me on my problems. This is not to say that everyone else at the Cavendish was working on radioactivity. The 'big shots' like G. I. Taylor, F. W. Aston, P. Kapitza, C. T. R Wilson and of course J. J. Thomson were not; nor were T. E Allibone, J. D. Cockcroft or E. T. S. Walton who were still relatively junior.

I had decided to put in for a prize fellowship at Trinity and therefore chose a job which I felt could be completed and written up in a year. I was interested in field emission because the electric fields were rather similar in magnitude to those developed across aluminium oxide films, which I had investigated as a schoolboy and later with Sanderson at the GEC labs. At that time it was thought that field emission was the same as the increase in thermionic electron emission that takes place as the positive voltage on the anode of a triode is increased, and which was explained by Schottky is due to the electric field at the cathode surface reducing the work done by an electron in escaping from the cathode. Fowler and Nordheim had not yet made their analysis which explained field emission as a 'tunneling' of electrons, treating the electrons as waves rather then particles. This made field emission analogous to frustrated internal reflection of light waves.

I decided to test Schottky's equation because no one had done so and it seemed it would be a fairly clear cut bit of investigation. Fortunately, Hull of the GE of Schenectady USA had presented Rutherford with a 30,000 volt DC power supply using full wave rectification by thermionic diodes. Unfortunately, the negative side was at high potential and the positive at earth. Cockcroft as usual came to my rescue and stood the whole cabinet on porcelain insulators and designed an input transformer with a gap of about five inches between the two windings each of which was toroid positioned as though each was a link in a chain. It worked, though it produced a lot of creepy noises due to corona discharges, and I verified Schottky's equation.

However, I was able to go a bit further because happily one of the tubes I made showed field emission and by subtracting the thermionic current I was able to show that the field emission was independent of temperature. Rutherford to my delight sponsored the paper and after his son-in-law, R. H. Fowler, had 'vetted' it with the comment 'at least we know what you've been up to', it was published in *Proceedings of the Royal Society* 120 (1928). I wrote up the work as a thesis for the Trinity fellowship.

J. J. Thomson was much more interested than Rutherford in what I was doing as might be expected from the father of the electron. But under a treaty between him and Rutherford he could not cross the demarcation line to visit me at work so that all our contacts had to be outside the Cavendish and as often as not were in King's Parade.

Tea time at the Cavendish was a tradition which J. J. Thomson started. It was open to everyone of graduate training but mostly attended by research workers. Rutherford did not carry on JJ's practice of attending, nevertheless it remained a social occasion in which one could get to know one's fellow workers. By the mid-1970s there were so many research workers that it took on more the appearance and noise of a cocktail party.

In his weekly visits Rutherford had told me that when he arrived back in the Cavendish in 1919 he found that JJ thought he could retain his professorship as well as becoming Master of Trinity College. Be that as it may I am afraid that Rutherford's boisterous sense of humour sometimes verged on bad taste as when he remarked to me, 'Pity that JJ does not wash more.' In old age we are apt to get careless of our appearance forgetting that the keen eyes of youth are searching us for material for jokes. Rutherford also pulled my leg by asking such questions as, 'Do you Patagonians still dye yourselves with woad?' Later when I became a fellow of Trinity College I was able to observe his boisterous behaviour among the dons at dinner, especially when he was sitting near Lapsley. 'What happens to a man when he becomes a Fellow? I see fine young men, who after a few years have green mould all over them.' Lapsley was a citizen of USA who had become a tutor at Trinity and was wholly anglicised and known for his preference for Etonian students; shortly after the unknown soldier was buried in Westminster Abbey, D. A. Winstanley referred to him as 'The Unknown Etonian.' Another member of the High Table who upset the history dons was J. B. S. Haldane, who in a loud voice might describe in some detail the effects of eating nothing but chalk for a week. Rutherford got no change out of quiet, witty Quaker Eddington. Rutherford told me that Einstein was 'one of those men whom Eddington has been pushing, you know, as a world wonder'. It is a fact, as has often been remarked, that relativity was far less important than quantum theory in physics at that time. Typical of Eddington is his reply to the question, 'Is it true that you and one other man are the only ones in England who understand relativity?' Eddington hesitated rather a long time and when the questioner urged him not to be modest Eddington replied, 'No it's not that; I was trying to think who the other man was.'

On the positive side I learned from Rutherford the importance of generosity about other people's work; not to go running around as a mini-angel of light making suggestions to others who either had already thought of and rejected them, or else were just about to think of them, and consequently felt robbed of priority, and above all to avoid biting criticism in case one should become another Thomas Young in the hands of a Lord Brougham.

During the time I was working at the Cavendish I got to know Blackett better. We had a common interest in technological matters; he was keenly interested in aircraft. I took him on a visit to the GEC labs of Wembley. He was intrigued when he heard that Punta Arenas was my birthplace; he knew it as the 'Paris of South America' from the days of the naval battle of the Falkland Isles. Blackett's experience at Göttingen and mine at Wembley made us look at the organisation of the Cavendish with somewhat critical eyes. He invited me to his home in Bateman Street. But I could not attune myself to his too idealistic left-wing outlook and when I argued he always replied with the cliché 'We can't put the clock back' which as Hayek has said 'expresses the fatalistic belief that we cannot learn from our mistakes, the most abject admission that we are incapable of using our intelligence.'[22]

The men and women scientists produced by the Cavendish were sometimes criticised (as were the pupils of Quincke, according to Pirani) for being untrained in the use of accurate instruments. Rutherford was quite unmoved by such criticism as he saw little merit in being able to take pointer readings on expensive equipment. At a meeting of the Cambridge Philosophical Society at which Professor Lowry announced that he had succeeded in measuring the index of refraction of some compound to one more decimal place, Rutherford rose saying he felt sure that all present would wish to join him in congratulating Professor Lowry and that he looked forward to the announcement next year by Professor Lowry that he had found it possible to take his researches one decimal point further yet.

A more serious criticism of our training was the absence of adequate mathematical instruction. We were expected to be able to write down differential equations such as that good old work horse:

$$\ddot{a}x + b\dot{x} + cx = 0$$

22. F. A. Hayek, *The Constitution of Liberty*, London 1976.

but were not expected to know just how the handles have to be turned to solve them. In this age of the computer such a philosophy makes even more sense than it did then, it suited me very well but not all were so happy with the system.

A character of paramount importance in the running of the Cavendish laboratory was Fred Lincoln, who had a waxed moustache with twisted, pointed ends that made him look like a recruiting sergeant of the Edwardian era. Originally a laboratory apprentice, he was brought up in the days when quite small amounts of money for research were extremely hard to come by. Many are the tales told of his harassment of research students. I remember one innocent newly-arrived from some far corner of the empire asking Lincoln for some sealing wax. Sealing wax and string were of course the legendary tools of research then. While Lincoln, as a gesture of good will, was looking for a few short lengths and odd bits, the innocent compounded his felony by adding, '"Bank of England" wax please'. Consternation spread over Lincoln's face and he shouted, 'Bank of England!' in a manner that made clear the enormity of the request.

I once went down to the workshop to ask Fred Lincoln to order a quantity of open-ended unsealed lamp bulbs from the General Electric Company; they cost a few pence each. He said nothing but at that moment Rutherford came in and Lincoln said, 'Sir, am I to get five dozen lamp bulbs for de Bruyne?' Rutherford replied in his loudest voice for all to hear that it was time de Bruyne realised the cost of research work. So I ordered them myself, there was no charge. I later told Lincoln that he had got to face up to the fact that we should be seeing quite a lot of one another and I suggested it might be less painful if we treated one another with mutual courtesy. The mechanic in the workshop overheard me and said how pleased he was that some one had stood up to Lincoln at last and he invited me to tea on Sunday; he and his wife had a university lodging house in Chesterton Road.

But later on I discovered something very fine in Lincoln's private life and came to respect him.

Monday morning was his worst time; that was when he had to work an infernal machine of which he was rightly terrified and which had a label on it: 'Presented by the Air Ministry'. Appropriately it made liquid air but made Lincoln suffer for every

6. Aero Research Ltd, Duxford, c. 1936.

7. The first Aero Research extension offical opening, 1936. *Left to right:* F. T. Hearle (managing director of de Havilland); Prof. B. M. Jones (Aero Research Committee); D. R. Pye (deputy director, Scientific Research Air Ministry); myself; C. C. Walker (chief engineer and director of de Havilland); Prof. G. I Taylor (Aero Research Committee); C. C. Paterson (chief of GEC research labs); W. S. Farren (Aero Research Committee).

8. The staff of Aero Research Ltd, 1938. *Left to right (standing):* George Newell, Riro Mooney, Frank Bird, Ron Mooney, H. Thomas, Leslie Mansfield, Bunt Touhey; (sitting) Robert Lea, Miss Gifford, Claude Rayner. Along with Wesley Coe and myself we formed the original team of twelve.

9. The original pilot plant for making Aerolite.

STABILISATION OF THIN SHEET METAL.

These three members of the staff at the Cambridge University Engineering Laboratory found they had a common interest and ability in solving the problems involved using Wagner's analysis. First people in England to use 'Wagner's Theory' on how to compute the strength of a fuselage using calculations of the dimensions of the wing and fuselage.

After pain staking work by Mrs Constance Tipper, and mathematical calculations by Gerald Gough, and practical experience by Norman de Bruyne in the building of his own aeroplane, of a 'controversial design' according to the men at Farnborough who rejected it outright, but after severe tests, the design was approved June 1935.

Their work was finally acknowledged, and revolutionised aeroplane construction in England.

11. An experimental Spitfire fuselage made with Gordon Aerolite.

drop. Every part of it vibrated and predicted an imminent explosion. Unfortunately I became the chief user of liquid air and quite often there was none by Thursday.

In our first year of research, we had instruction in workshop practice. All the lathes, except that used by the mechanic, were treadle operated and had a slide rest on which one held a hand tool. We were taught how to lacquer brass, how to use a file, and how to cut a thread with a chasing tool.

In September 1928 I was elected a prize fellow of Trinity College, which gave me free rooms, free dinner, and four hundred pounds a year for four years, one of which could be spent abroad. The other two successful candidates were R. P. Winnington Ingram and W. L. Edge. There were no restrictions of any kind; but those who did nothing found themselves unwanted at the end of the four years. I felt I had joined the best club in the world and was being paid for it too. What a wonderful body of men – J. J. Thomson, Rutherford, Eddington, Trevelyan, Adrian, Robertson, Nicholas, Ellis, Winstanley, Housman, Hardy, Littlewood, Pantin and at one time Bertrand Russell and many others were one's companions at the end of the day. These were great men, some great in character, some great in discovery, some great in friendship, some great in all three.

At about this time I began to experiment with coated filaments to see if the field emission could be increased. One of the materials I tried was caesium, which Langmuir had shown greatly increased the thermionic emission. A rather striking experiment was that if the filament was too hot for the caesium to stay on the tungsten, then on switching off the heating current the thermionic emission could be seen to rise. Rutherford asked me to show this at the Royal Society Conversazione of 15 May 1929.

I got the impression that Rutherford was not too pleased about the fellowship perhaps because his own candidate was not elected and would therefore require financial support. Winstanley told me that R. H. Fowler, who worked closely with his father-in-law, had asked (though not on the election committee) to see my thesis before the election and that he had refused the request. Or perhaps it was just that Rutherford felt JJ had scored a victory over him.

Anyway when Rutherford congratulated me he took much of the joy out of it by adding, 'Well now you can give your time to helping with the teaching.' But I continued my work and proved to my satisfaction that Millikan was wrong in saying that field emission was not independent of temperature above 1000°K. When I asked Rutherford if I should publish my results in the *Physical Review* (a US journal) he said, 'Yes if you're sure of them, but don't be surprised if you get a rocket back'. My paper appeared in *Physical Review* 35 (1930) 172-5. No rocket arrived. My hazy recollection is that Millikan visited the Cavendish some time later and when I asked him whether he was still working on field emission he replied that he regarded it as a worked-out subject.

However I got a rocket from Rutherford, who instructed me to work with H. C. Webster to investigate a claim by some professor in USA that alpha particles interacted with an electronic space charge. Rutherford said it seemed to him to be inconceivable; nevertheless, someone had to repeat the work. I was happy to help Webster just as I did other members of the staff and the following extract is relevant to this:

> About the middle of the 1929 came our introduction to be thyratron. A. W. Hull, of the American GEC, who was visiting the Cavendish, gave us first-hand information about it which made it clear that here was just the device needed for automatic recording. The thyratron could be tripped by a fleeting positive impulse from an amplifier, even of only a few microseconds' duration. The subsequent large arc current could operate a robust mechanical counting meter, and it would continue to flow until the anode circuit was interrupted by the meter when recording was completed. The next slide (Hull 1929, figure 39) shows the diagram of a single thyratron counting circuit which appeared in Hull's paper. Incidentally, this particular slide has been projected very many times at the Royal Institution during Rutherford's lectures.
>
> While we were still pessimistically wondering how long it would be before we could lay hands on one of these new thyratrons, a Cavendish enthusiast, N. A. de Bruyne, had opened up an old T.15 transmitting valve, introduced a globule of mercury, evacuated, baked out and sealed off the valve. He proudly presented this to us with the casual remark, 'Here's a thyratron for you'. So, within a few days of the talk with Hull, we were able to verify that a thyratron really could be used for automatically counting ex-particles. Unfortunately, before de Bruyne's thyratron could be used on a live experiment, it met with a sad accident a day or two later, when lent to another Cavendish enthusiast. In due course, however, the B.T.H. Co. kindly

> presented the Cavendish with some thyratrons, and de Bruyne and Webster (1931) successfully used single-thyratron counters for automatic recording with their Geiger counters.[23]

Rutherford was very fond of using the single-thyratron counter at his Royal Institution lectures. The changing dial figures, the sharp click of the mechanism and the bright flash of the arc, all helped to convey to the audience that ex-particles really were being counted. Reporters, however, sometimes missed the point, for one morning, the following statement appeared in a leading newspaper: 'Last night, at the Royal Institution, Lord Rutherford disintegrated the atom with a blue flash and a noise like rapid machine-gun fire!'

But my attitude to repeating the US professor's work was much like that of Blackett's attitude on another occasion, 'If physics laboratories have to be run dictatorially . . . I would rather be my own dictator.'

So I took my MA and PhD degrees in 1930 and concluded that this was the end of my time at the Cavendish. At the *viva voce* exam for my PhD, Rutherford asked what colour I mentally gave an electron.

The following is an extract from a letter from P. Kapitza dated July 1964 to his contemporaries at the Cavendish:

> What a wonderful time it was then at the Cavendish! The science belonged to the scientists and not to the politicians. Nowadays in spite of the terrific amount of money which is available for science, we do not enjoy our work nearly as much as in the old days. The young generation will never know how pleasant the scientific work was in those days. Your letter reminded me of the old days and I am thankful to you for it.

Fortunately, Trinity College came to my rescue, and for those unfamiliar with the intricacies of British institutions, that may represent the adaptations and growth of centuries. I must explain that the relation of the University of Cambridge to the colleges is somewhat similar to that of the federal government in USA to the separate states. Trinity asked me if I would like to take over the job of Junior

23. N. A. de Bruyne and H. C. Webster, *Proceedings of the Cambridge Phil. Society,* Vol. 27 (1931).

Bursar (as Gowland Hopkins had and Cockcroft would at St John's in the future) as something to keep the wolf from the door while I looked around. So in September 1931, at the age of 26, I became Junior Bursar of Trinity College, Cambridge. To put this in perspective I reminded myself that William Pitt Junior was prime minister, and Lawrence Bragg a Nobel prize winner, at this age.

When I told my father, he commented briefly, 'Don't expect me to congratulate you!' But I saw the job as the first step in the realisation of my early Edisonian ambitions. 'Jabez' Cooper's final comment was ever in my mind: 'Of his ultimate success I have little doubt, though I think it will be in applied rather than pure science'. While a Junior Bursar's job was no sinecure it would give me time and money for other activities. My office hours in term time were 10:00 to 1:00 pm and 6:00 to 9:00 pm.

I had obtained my pilot's 'A' license in 1929. My introduction to private flying was made in a curious way. Rev. F. A. Simpson a fellow of Trinity College, history don, clergyman, a former colleague of W. M. Howitt at Oxford, and a well known eccentric, had bought himself a de Havilland Moth aeroplane. Too old to fly it himself he got various RAF pilots (Atcherley, Boyle and Johnson) to fly it around and one of them took me up one afternoon from Marshall's Aerodrome at Cambridge. I had been in an aeroplane in 1921 flying from Amsterdam (Schiphol) to London (Croydon) in a KLM Fokker. I soon felt airsick but managed to open a window in time not to embarrass myself and the other two passengers.

This Moth flight was different. It was obviously a private owner's machine; it gave me a feeling of intense exhilaration and access to a new world in the sky waiting to be explored. When I came down people were behaving as though nothing had happened; did they not realise that mankind now had wings? I determined to learn to fly. Fortunately, after graduating at Jesus College, and getting a 'blue' for running, young Arthur Marshall (later Sir Arthur Marshall OBE DL) had started a flying school at the back of his father's house on the Newmarket Road. I was his first pupil and after getting my license bought a de Havilland Moth from him (GAAWN). I subsequently got a ground engineer's license and an aircraft welder's license (welding is much easier than glass blowing). In December, 1929, I accompanied Arthur Marshall in his Moth GAAEH on a flight to Dresden and back before Christmas. The spirit of those carefree days has been captured in David Garnett's book, *A Rabbit in the Air.*[24]

When I had written this chapter on the Cavendish Laboratory I sent a copy to Tress Nicholas then 92 years old, formerly Senior Bursar of Trinity College. Here is the substance of his reply:

Dear Norman,

What a mine of delight are your Xerox papers! I do hope that they mean you are writing up your life for publication? have you any objection to my showing them to one or two people who would be interested? Charles Oatley for instance and John Bradfield (who was Junior Bursar before he succeeded me)? Patrick Duff and Harry Sandbach are the only two fellows left who were elected before 1928.

The few pages explain all sorts of things I only dimly – or wrongly – knew before.

For instance I hadn't realised your admiration for J J. ' Who was his assistant in later years? The man who according to fable assured Lady Thomson on the phone that he had noticed nothing peculiar about Sir James's dress when he arrived at the lab, in reply to her information that they had found the new trousers she put out to make him wear, having, as she thought hidden the old ones where he wouldn't be able to find them. Was this Hayles, rhyming with 'smiles' or Everett?

I knew that your relations with Rutherford were prejudiced by your declining to join the radioactivity band wagon. The current rumour in Trinity was that when he said he hadn't funds to pay for your apparatus you told him you would pay for it yourself. It was just at the moment when the Rouse Ball American Trust money was being paid over to the College and Trinity had for the first time a large sum specifically for research and the Council decided that the first charge on it should be the dividends of Title A fellows, leaving the balance for grants. The 'greybook' of College Accounts shows that the first grant (£94) was made in 1927/28 followed by £2294 in grants in 1928/29. Did you ever get anything from it then, or later?

A piece of hearsay about the 1928 fellowship Election was that Rutherford said it was to your credit that you were the first chap in his laboratory who had the courage to defy him, which did not go unnoticed by the non-scientific electors! A slightly later case of Rutherford failing to get his man elected was in 1930, when I was

24 David Garnett, *A Rabbit in the Air,* London 1932 (from a diary kept while learning to handle an aeroplane).

myself an Elector. It was still in the period when candidates had to take examination papers on the 'Principles of Knowledge' and 'General Aspects of Literature, Art and History.' There was a terrific hassle for the last place between Mr 'B' and Rutherford's Mr 'A'; in a straw vote. The votes were equal and we turned to the Examination Papers. 'B' had written reams about Gothic Architecture, Music, Ethics, Old Masters and so on, 'A' an Australian had written nothing, so the final vote went to 'B' and 'A' went, I think to Birmingham.

Simpson used to pretend he couldn't remember Rutherford's name, when having to refer to him he would after some pretence of trying to recall it say, 'You know, that man with the loud voice.' Rutherford after being subjected to what he considered unduly high brow conversation in Hall would exclaim in his booming voice 'Well, who's coming with me to see the Marx Brothers?'.

Apropos, of your Rutherford remark – new to me – about 'green mould' growing on young Trinity Fellows, it is thoroughly in keeping with my memories of him for he was continually urging young men to leave Cambridge and get some experience of the world outside before coming to senior posts. I recall him vividly, getting to his feet at one of the long series of Saturday afternoon College Meetings we had to have to approve all the long list of new Statutes made for us by the Statutory Commission in 1926 or more truthfully, by their Secretary Harry Hollond.

One of these Statutes was to do with tenure of Fellowship and in those days it was normal for the college staff to be recruited from the junior research Fellows – we made occasional appointments from other colleges or elsewhere but they were rare. (Now that is quite changed. I guess, without researching into it, that more than half our teaching come from other colleges now) – I remember him saying to the Meeting, 'You get a young chap, he does a good bit of research, and he gets a Fellowship. And he's here for life, for LIFE Master'. As the supreme example at present of that state of affairs I'm glad to acknowledge the wisdom of Rutherford's view in the old days, when the College had much less money and we couldn't afford to add to the customary number of the teaching staff, frightful enmities used to develop when a vacancy occurred and several subjects had a blue-eyed boy among the Title A Fellows which they each wanted to get on to the staff. Now things are much easier and we can also get really first class research people into the College as Title B Fellows with no teaching responsibilities. Your reference to Winstanley's remark about

Lapsley needs a trifle emendation, it was Westminster Abbey, not the Cenotaph where the Unknown Soldier was interred after World War I. 'One of Nature's Etonians' was also a current phrase about Lapsley.

Do you remember Rouse Ball's 'Tuesday lunches'? Every week in full term a highly formal lunch at 'Elmside' was laid on with waiters etc., a Master of a College, 2 or 3 Professors and college lecturers, all with wives and any interstices were filled up by young Title A Fellows, invited at shorter notice. After lunch the party moved into the Billiard Room where Rouse Ball demonstrated his latest mechanical toy. I particularly remember one occasion when the toy was 'Radio Rex' a metal dog kennel from which a spring ejected a dog on being shouted at. Among the guests that day were G. I. Taylor and J. B. S. Haldane who was discoursing loudly at the back of the assembled crowd. The toy wouldn't work and Rouse Ball grew quite testy. 'It worked perfectly before lunch, I assure you' but the dog couldn't be got to stay in his kennel and came out immediately when Rouse Ball withdrew his hand. G. I. suggested 'Send Haldane out of the room' and as soon as he retired, the dog stayed in his kennel until Rouse Ball called to him. Someone once said that Haldane 'talked on the intake as well as the exhaust'. He once in Hall said in answer to some question, 'That is a matter on which I am voiceless' and the still small voice of Broad was heard to say 'Paradoxical as that might appear'. I remember Lapsley being so put off by one of Haldane's descriptions at dinner of his symptoms after taking large quantities of some substance that he rose in stately manner to his feet and walked out of Hall.

I was amused by your story about Eddington and relativity, I had never heard it. I remember him as a regular diner in Hall who never spoke a word unless in answer to a question.

Did you ever hear Thirkhill talk about JJ and how a cheque for his quarterly stipend was signed by JJ while Thirkhill held it round the large lamp-post which stood at the corner of Benet Street and King's Parade, lending JJ his pen for the purpose, on a winter's evening just before Christmas. I wonder if you ever saw an article Charlie Ellis wrote about Rutherford for the *Trinity Review* in 1960. I've got a spare copy and will enclose it with this. Love to Elma and apologies for bad writing.

P.S. I've decided to send you Air Mail (Printed paper rate) a small book on the second revolution in Geology brought about by physicists during the last 20 years.

I believe the most important work I was involved in, with two colleagues (Mrs Constance Tipper nee Elam, and Gerald Gough) whilst at the Cavendish, was our work on the stabilisation of thin sheet metal.

A paper was published in 1939 in the Royal Aeronautical Journal, but the full impact and importance of our work was not realised until much later. Our work was to greatly influence and, in fact, revolutionise the future construction of modern aircraft.

Sadly, Gough died at a young age. Mrs Tipper became involved, on behalf of the Admiralty, during the 1940s, in 'Fractures occurring in all-welded ships'. Her work 'The Brittle Fracture Story' was published in 1960 by the C.U.P. Sadly, Constance Tipper died in December 1995 aged 101.

CHAPTER SIX

JUNIOR BURSAR

THE duties of a Junior Bursar were not clearly defined in the way that such a job in industry would have to be. The college statutes amongst other things required him to read out a passage beginning 'Let us now praise famous men' from Ecclesiastes at the annual commemoration day service in chapel. And the Master and the Junior Bursar had jointly to interview all newly-appointed bedmakers; this was in accordance with the tradition that bedmakers must be 'nec pulchra nec juvenis' (neither pretty nor young). I also attended the funerals of all college servants; salvation army funerals were by far the most emotional.

Briefly described, the Junior Bursar's job was to run a hotel (except for the catering side of such a business). He was responsible to the College Council which met every Friday morning in term time. He was secretary of a number of committees, such as the Gardens Committee the Wine Committee, the Combination-Room Committee (the Combination Room is the Fellows' common room and had nothing to do with combinations). I was also a member of the Estates Committee which was one of the Senior Bursar's committees, the other member was Sir W. C. Dampier Whethem of Upwater Lodge, Riverside, Cambridge. In the long vacation there was always a major building operation going on. In my time New Court, Nevile's Court, part of Great Court, and the fountain in Great Court were repaired, and the whole of Whewell's Court was rewired by one man, Mr Bell, who afterwards became clerk of the works. Under-floor heating was installed in the chapel and in the course of work, Bentley's skull was unearthed and reintered.

It was a most useful experience to me, particularly being on the College Council and observing the great men in action. J. J.

Thomson, the Master, was the chairman; he felt it his duty sometimes to be severe even to the point of almost accusing members of acting *ultra vires*. But there was not a trace of ill will in it and no one was upset. The man with a gift for unbiassed clear exposition of a difficult subject was the senior tutor, J. R. M. Butler, son of the former Master, and at one time member of Parliament for Cambridge University. I remember showing him a letter from one of the tutors complaining in no uncertain terms about some triviality or other and he commented, 'The paradox is that those who are most sensitive about their own feelings being hurt are themselves unduly provocative'. And when I later had a success with de Havilland and had to ask the Council's permission to enter into a contract he said, 'You have cast your bread very successfully on the waters de Bruyne.'

The minutes of the meetings, written by the senior bursar, were masterpieces of correctness and uniformativeness; this was because they were circulated to all the fellows and experience had shown that too much detail led to misunderstandings. Later on I remembered this when drafting minutes of my own company which had to be circulated to the majority shareholder, CIBA of Basle, Switzerland.

Some matters had to be referred to a 'college meeting' attended by all the fellows. It was always hard to get any firm resolution passed at a college meeting.

We had a series of meetings about the lighting of the dining hall. It was no use quoting the Latin tag 'De gustisbus nil disputandum'. Finally A. S. F. Gow in a master stroke, put the following motion :'As an experiment in order to give more time for consideration of the problem, I propose we have simple pendants with calf-skin shades.' With a sigh of relief this motion was agreed to; and the shades hung there for years. I noticed that they have now given place to silver candlesticks fitted with electric light bulbs and standing on the tables.

The devious thinking of academic minds has been analysed in a little book of wisdom by Cornford, who was professor of Greek. Here is an example: 'I was in favour of the proposal until I heard Mr ________'s argument in support of it.'[25]

25. F. M. Cornford, *Microcosmographia Academica: Being a Guide for the Young Academic Politician*, 4th edn, Cambridge 1949, p. 18.

Cambridge colleges (perhaps because the bursars were basically academics, and only amateur administrators, whereas at Oxford the policy was just the reverse) were always better looked after than Oxford colleges. The work of maintaining old buildings is never ending and is expensive. On the advice of T. C. Nicholas I got in touch with Mr W. R. Dean of the University Estate Management Department who introduced me to a procedure which greatly simplified the costing of day-to-day maintenance. This consisted of a bulky schedule covering every conceivable maintenance job; it was sent out annually to builders with costs prepared by a quantity surveyor. The builder was asked to give an overall percentage figure for his profit. Once a builder had been selected it was only necessary to measure up the work and payment could be made without more ado. How it would function in these inflationary times I do not know.

Membership of the estates committee was interesting. Historically, and still wisely, a large part of the college investments were in real property. The most troublesome was agricultural property; there was little or no possibility of getting much rent. One had to give abatements to persuade the farmer to retain his tenancy. Now the situation is, I imagine, reversed in the college's favour; though not in the individual investor's favour since so much of what he gets is taken away by taxation. The Inland Revenue invented a specially pejorative name for such income – 'unearned income'. T. C. Nicholas had initiated a policy of buying the freeholds of banks and multiple shops such as Woolworth and leasing the property back to the occupants; this was successful. Even more successful, as events have turned out, was his purchase of a large estate near Felixstowe Port which because it managed to evade nationalisation became a profitable undertaking.

I learned that one should not buy property adjacent or opposite to a church because after dark it makes a big black hole in what should be a brightly lit shopping centre.

I learned of the value of investing in USA. It was this policy pursued by Rouse Ball which had greatly increased the wealth of the college. Its value was also shown of course when devaluation occurred.

It was a golden period in my life. Every afternoon I would bicycle along the Newmarket Road to see how my aeroplane was getting on (see next chapter.)

Nevertheless, after six years and having reached the age of 33, when one realises that one's life is not infinite, I decided to get back to research and teaching and in 1937 I was appointed a college lecturer in mechanical sciences and university demonstrator. This entailed giving a course of lectures on physics to first-year engineers as well as a course of lectures on plastics to senior engineers and also becoming a director of studies in Trinity. I was given a room in Scroope House for research, but the professor of engineering Ingals told me bluntly that he regarded research as a luxury and that the job of his staff was to teach undergraduates. Nevertheless he allotted me a small room for research. My senior colleague in Trinity was G. S. Gough, a quiet man with great ability who took an intimate interest in what I was doing in structural research and was an enormous help to me. He had been on the staff of the Southern Railway and was the only member of the staff who had practised engineering as a profession. One of the feelings of the Cambridge Engineering Department was that unlike continental engineering schools it had no contact with industry. When the war broke out he took over all my duties to give me freedom to do research work, but after a year or so wrote me the saddest letter I had ever received, saying that he had got encephalitis. He died on 20 February 1943, at the age of 46. When discussing this with Adrian, he said that he had known for some time from the rigidity of the expression on Gough's face that there was brain damage.

I was able to talk to Gough most evenings at Trinity, and it was Gough who recommended Mrs Tipper (nee Elam) as the person who could help with my research on Wagner's analysis. Mrs Tipper carried out the laborious task of making and testing the springs, a lengthy and painstaking process, while Gough finished the necessary mathematics understanding Wagner's work. Mrs Tipper never received recognition from the people she had worked with, because she was a woman, but her work on showing up the failure in American ships which were bringing necessary parts to England at the time, was published by herself in her book (*The Brittle Fracture Story* CUP 1962). She had shown that the failure was not in the steel, but in the way it was used. In 1995 she celebrated her 101st birthday.

I resigned my appointment as college lecturer and fellow of Trinity College in 1944 when I realised that the war had so changed my outlook that I could never return to an academic life despite all its attractions and importance; I had already, in 1942, written to the master G. M. Trevelyan (1876-1962) expressing my wish to become a fellow without dividend. The Master, G. M. Trevelyan (1876-1962) wrote me the following letter:

The Master's Lodge
Trinity College
Cambridge
March 3, 1944

Dear de Bruyne,

I read your letter to the council of the College today and they accepted with regret your resignation. Nicholas asked us to accept as from March 31st, not March 25th as you said, because March 31st is the F.S.S.U. date.

The council asked me to express to you its strong sense of obligation, not only for your teaching work but especially for your work for the College as Junior Bursar. May I add my own strong feeling on the subject.

Yours Sincerely

G M Trevelyan

CHAPTER SEVEN

THE SNARK

I HAD begun to take an interest in aircraft construction in 1931. After an abortive week at Handley Page, I spent that summer at the de Havilland Aeronautical Technical School as an owner pilot-apprentice. The de Havilland Aeronautical Technical School was started in 1928 primarily to give some theoretical training to their apprentices. Mr E. P. King gave me lessons in aircraft 'stressing' (computing the strength of aircraft structures) ranging from the theorem of three moments of beams to detailed design of aircraft fittings to ensure that the bolts would cause simultaneous bearing, shear and tension failure in sheet metal fittings! Alan Eadon, in charge of the apprentices, told me that Mr Walker would be glad to have a general talk with me about aircraft design but I foolishly did not do anything about it; I had no idea, until I met him some years later, what I had missed.

The de Havilland aircraft company was then at Stag Lane Aerodrome (which was somewhat hilly) and financially it was at the bottom of a depression. The technical position on the other hand was excellent. The Tiger Moth (biplane) flew on 25 October 1931; it was destined to become the basic trainer of all the commonwealth countries. The Puss Moth had made its first flight in March 1930. What distinguished the de Havilland Co. from the other British aircraft companies was the reality of its approach to its market. De Havilland, between the wars, practically refused to make military aircraft. In fact, the military production was just twenty aircraft between the wars.

The more I learned the more convinced I became that there was room for original work in a branch of aeronautics that seemed to have gotten into a rut. It is difficult to recall how conservative most British aircraft structures were in that period. Thick wings were thought to have a large drag. Cantilever wings were thought to be too heavy or even too risky. Anything but a biplane was regarded as un-English and not really practical.

Nowhere was orthodoxy more firmly entrenched than in the Airworthiness Department of the Royal Aircraft Establishment (RAE) where for instance all the stress analysis forms were over-printed for biplanes only.

After making two false starts with B. B. Henderson and with R. E. Bishop, I decided to 'go it alone'. In designing the box type fuselage I used Herbert Wagner's tension field analysis (then almost unknown in England), and by applying strain gauges to a dummy section of a plywood covered wing, I found that the load on the two spars was almost unaffected by the position of the centre of pressure and by designing the spars on the basis of plastic failure (using W. Prager's analysis) I produced a design with a weight below that required by conventional stress analysis. I called the aeroplane the 'Snark', and I called myself the Cambridge Aeroplane Construction Company. I took on the late S. Wilkinson as qualified ground engineer but after about eighteen months he got fed up and left so I became a qualified ground engineer and welder and took on a lad named Sheldrick.

The Airworthiness Dept of the RAE threw out the whole concept. They could not issue a certificate for such a light structure. The fuselage in particular could not possibly stand the required loads; as evidence they produced a list of all existing monocoque fuselages, to show that they were all of heavier construction than mine; undoubtedly they were. The refusal of the RAE to accept my design led to an impasse which was opened up by K. T. Spencer (later chief scientist of the Ministry of Fuel and Power) who persuaded the 'superintendent' (i.e. the head of the RAE) to buy a fuselage from me and test it to destruction. The test was carried out on 13 June 1934, and the results increased my unpopularity considerably; they were published without mentioning my name in R & M 1694. The design was approved on 21 June 1934 by the Airworthiness Department. At about the same time Roxbee Cox (later Lord Kings Norton) made an analysis of the division of load between the spars in a stressed skin wing and I was able to use it in designing the wings.

I changed my business name from Cambridge Aeroplane Construction Company to Aero Research Ltd in April 1934 and just about then was joined by George S Newell. In a speech I made at the annual works dinner of Aero Research Ltd on 23 October 1954, I said,

> When George Newell and I started together twenty years ago we were happy and thrilled to work in a bare corrugated iron shed in a field off the Newmarket Road, which was Marshall's aerodrome at that time. We were both fairly young but he was a bit younger – in fact, 16 years old and he came straight from being head prefect at the Cambridge Tech. Why he came I cannot think. It could not have been our pension scheme or our sports and social activities or the promise of a house. It certainly was not the money which was ten shillings a week – subject (as he recently reminded me) to a deduction of one shilling and seven pence. It must have been the lure of aircraft, and really there are not many pleasanter ways for a young man to spend his time than making aeroplanes. He soon showed his ability and I always remember the way in which he persuaded plywood to assume double curvature on the DB3. From there he went on to undertake an enormous volume of testing and construction work. His outstanding speed, initiative, skill and common sense have been of tremendous value to the firm.

Meanwhile, regardless of the RAE I had begun to make the Snark in a shed rented from Arthur Marshall, and on the 16 December 1934, it was ready for its first flight. All went well until I was over the Cambridge Gas Works, when the engine spluttered – but almost immediately picked up again. On the next take-off, the engine, after revving at full throttle in the usual way on the ground, cut out completely leaving me just room to land inside the aerodrome. The flexible tube to the carburettor was found to be full of dirt. On the third flight the Snark, when taxying, tried to stand on its nose and broke its propeller. So back to the drawing board again and a re-design of the undercarriage was made. As I got to know the machine I appreciated its exceptional rate of climb and ease of take-off. It was a joy to hold it at a few feet above the ground, well above the stalling speed, and then spring into the air.

I only had one anxious moment of it subsequently and that was when I encountered flutter on flaps, which I had fitted experimentally to try to increase the drag on landing. The Snark's fault was that it was much easier to get into the air than out of it.

After a full load diving test at Marshall's Aerodrome in March 1935, I took the machine to Martlesham to get official approval and a certificate of air-worthiness. The regulations required me to do each test myself first. Nevertheless, the sergeant pilot who had to repeat each test, floated the Snark right across the airfield in trying to land. He could not believe that the indicated stalling speed near the ground could be less than 30 m.p.h.

I flew the Snark (GADDL) with my brother Bernard and his wife, Mary de Bruyne, to Berlin calling on 'Oom Wig' on the way out and, in April 1936, I sold the machine to the Air Ministry who had it stationed at Duxford RAF Aerodrome for research work by B. Melvill Jones, and J. A. G. Haslam. Its merit for this work was its thick wing.

The following is an excerpt from a letter from Rev. J. A. G. Haslam, dated 28 February 1967:

> I ought to be able to do better for the Snark than I can – I mean I don't remember flying other aeroplanes. Was it a very undemanding aeroplane? That is rather my overall impression (and by the way I hope that I didn't even 'guesstimate' my time on the Snark as 120 or 130 hours as Arthur M gave it to you – it was 60 hours in 67 'flights', including very short ones, tests and so on). But it must be said that I had already accepted that an aeroplane with a 4-cylinder engine would shake more than one with a 12-cylinder and that the structure did not allow the same tautness of control and stable flight as the Hart had. I never succeeded in holding the Snark so steady for speed and altitude as I could hold the Hart, but it would do as well as it could – and well enough for our purposes, on the whole – in an easy, relaxed way (to run aeroplane and pilot through one another).
>
> I have a much less-clear picture of the Snark with me flying it than of other aeroplanes – I don't know why at all. One strong impression is of the view ahead being less open between 10 and 11:30 (clock reference) than I would have liked – the cowling etc. coming 2 or 3 inches high, largely due to my parachute and I think this was particularly noticeable when approaching fully throttled to land and may have accentuated the unwillingness one felt to keep down to a speed that avoided a lot of float before one could pull the stick back and sit down. (Were you at RAF Duxford when the Martlesham pilot did the formal 'acceptance test' and took about 3 shots to get her down inside the aerodrome? He didn't take to her – hadn't the time really – and handed over to me saying, 'all right, have her if you want her').
>
> On better acquaintance I realized that the Snark suffered (unjustifiably to a great extent) from being different, but had a remarkable

performance for its power and load, was easily controllable to anything but a very high standard of exactitude of regime, including flying by instruments only, and probably could be operated from a smaller airfield than comparable current types so long as an open approach to land could be found in order to exploit the slow (flat) glide and consequent short run. The take-off and climb with two on board was remarkable and very welcome for our research flights which often had to be done round 10,000 ft. to get calm air. I'm confident that the Snark was never unserviceable for any 'aeroplane' fault while we had it and I never had any complaint about difficulty of maintenance. For travelling flights I should have to give preference to the Puss Moth – the high wing and narrow nose gave the best pilot-navigator position I know (not strictly navigator – I don't know a word for the one who finds the way by pilotage mainly, since pilot has come to mean the one who controls the aeroplane), but I would like to have had the opportunity to repeat some of my Shell journeys by Puss Moth with the Snark instead.

I notice two entries in the Remarks space (very limited) in my Log Book – one for a flight of 60 min. (with an RAF Sergeant as passenger – ?Sgt. pilot) 'trying sideslip and approaches and control generally', the other for a flight of 25 min. (with an RAF Corporal as passenger – I think N.C.O. i/c rigging for the Snark), 'approaches with 'sinking' as method of varying rate of loss of height'. The latter confirms my memory trial the Snark had a considerable range of easily manageable stalled flight, free from sudden wing dropping. I was always interested in the possibility of this type of approach but few aeroplanes allowed any attempt to explore it. The former entry seems to recall that if I used side-slip to regulate the approach on the Snark, I was apt to get the cowling blocking the view of the area in which I was aiming to land; so I was trying to find a 'routine' for side-slip approach which avoided this difficulty.

To sum up this long and incoherent account of flying the Snark, let me say I enjoyed it very much; and when I reflect that it was the one and only – without benefit of development – I am filled with admiration for it (to avoid the embarrassment of another pronoun!).

The experiments on the Snark were in the line of those arising from Melvill Jones' paper on 'The Streamline Aeroplane' (1929).[26] Following this paper, the improvements in design of aeroplanes so far reduced their drag due to obstructions of one kind and another, that skin friction drag (profile drag of wings) became a significant item in total drag, and its measurement and reduction items for exploration.

26. B. Melvill Jones, 'The Streamline Aeroplane', *Journal of the Royal Aeronautical Society*, Vol. 33 (1929), pp. 357–85.

> Experiments at Cambridge produced the pilot-traverse method of measuring wing profile drag in flight and were developed at Farnborough (RAE), giving data on a number of wing sections.
> The conclusion had been reached that smooth thick wings have a lower drag coefficient in actual flight conditions than would have been predicted from wind,-tunnel-experiments.
> One of the objects sought in purchasing the Snark was thus to provide further data on the profile drag of thick wings in flight. Another was to extend experiments begun on a 'Hart' aeroplane (RAF 28 wing section) to develop a method of locating the boundary layer transition point in flight and to explore the influence of various factors on its position, with a view to reducing profile drag by increasing layer flow, by delaying transition to the turbulent form.
> The experiments made on the 'Hart' and 'Snark' showed that the transition point can be located by means of simple apparatus and technique. Analysis of the measured conditions under which transition occurred did not yield any basis for predicting the transition point.'

On completion of the research work the Snark was put up for sale by the Air Ministry and bought by Peter Masefield in collaboration I believe with Thurstan James and F. D. Bradbrooke all of *The Aeroplane.* Then World War II removed all prospects of peaceful flying.

One feature in the Snark which I now think was a mistake was the provision for folding the wings. It added 160 pounds to the weight, as well as much expense and labour, and in fact I never folded the wings. It might have been improved by the provision of spoilers.

George Newell and I then started on the construction of the 'Ladybird' which was a mid-wing-, single-seat machine with a tricycle undercarriage and a semi-tapered twisted wing. It was intended to be a low-cost machine. About this time I began my association with the de Havilland Aircraft Company and I sold the partly finished machine to a young Dutchman J. N. Maas, who eventually went to work for Koolhoven at Rotterdam and was killed in the German bombing and invasion.

Flight magazine, (8 September 1938,p.204) has a picture of the completed machine. Test flights were carried out by R. G. Doig, originally with a Scott 'Flying Squirrel' engine and subsequently with a Bristo 'Cherub', which was a 43 HP flat twin designed by

Specification and performance of the Snark (Gypsy Major engine)

Empty weight, including instruments and upholstery		1,178 lb
Four occupants		680 lb
32 Imperial gallons of petrol		247 lb
Two Imperial gallons of oil		18 lb
Luggage		77 lb
		2,200 lb
Wing area		238.5 sq. ft
Span		42.5 ft
Wing loading		9.3 lb/sq. ft
Top speed	(at 2,200 lb)	123 mph
Cruising speed	(at 2,200 lb)	110 mph
Land speed	(at 2,200 lb)	38 mph
Ceiling	(at 2,200 lb)	17,000 ft
Initial rate of climb	(at 2,200 lb)	650 ft/min.

no less a person than Roy Fedden. The Ladybird had a single spar which also did duty as a dashboard where it passed through the cockpit. The span was 32 ft; wing area, 106 sq. ft; empty weight was 420 lb. It was mostly built by G. S. Newell and finished by N. J. Maas. It made its first flight on 6 January 1938, piloted by R. G. Doig at the new Marshall's Cambridge airport.

CHAPTER EIGHT

AERO RESEARCH LTD

On 7 April 1934 I formed Aero Research Ltd with a nominal capital of £100 and in May 1935 moved out from Marshall's (original) aerodrome to the village of Duxford where I had bought a fifty acre field and erected a second-hand steel-framed hangar with a width just greater than that of the wing-span of the Snark.

My idea was to act as a freelance consultant and research organisation in which I could carry my particular skills and knowledge into industry and particularly aeronautics. Looking back at the venture in 1959, I wrote,

> In recent years economists have increasingly studied the real behaviour of businessmen in making their decisions ... and as a contribution to the new approach I would like to emphasise the possible significance of the role of the guardian angel in business life.
>
> My own experience extends back over fifty years when I had a blond guardian angel over my bed. I now appreciate that she was a nice German girl with wings of low aspect ratio – quite different from those ethereal Italian angels with whom I got familiar later on. At school they told me that angels were masculine and I lost interest in them, but as so often happens, ideas rejected as intellectually unattractive are seen later to have an allegorical significance which in a sense restores their value.
>
> There is much to be said for the theory that there has been an guardian angel, or, at the very least, a fairy godmother looking after this firm. How else can one easily explain our survival and growth, despite the astonishing naive way in which we have gone about our business? ... We began by walking into a shop in Chancery Lane and buying articles of association empowering us *inter alia* to operate dirigibles.[27]

A site was found in the village of Duxford as a result of a careful

27. My preface to C. A. A. Rayner, *Milestones in the History of CIBA (A.R.L.) Limited* (1934–59), Cambridge 1959.

study of the 'For Sale' columns in the back pages of the *Cambridge Daily News*. I know that it was a careful study as I was, in fact, looking for a bandsaw. I cycled out one Saturday afternoon and the land was cheap, flat, reasonably near Cambridge, with ample water below, and electricity. I bought it little realising I had found what Ciba later described as an ideal site.

In those days, England was still a relatively free country and there were few brakes on enterprise. One could sink a well or fell a tree without getting official permission, put up any type of building almost anywhere for any purpose, provided it was in accordance with the local building regulations. Ideas could be made to materialise at surprising speed.

Duxford was the dullest village imaginable; almost the only children were those boarded out with foster parents. The best farm buildings were about sixty years old, which was about the last time that farming had been profitable. There was no mains water or sewage or street lighting, but thanks to private enterprise there was a mains electricity supply laid by the North Metropolitan Electric Company in cables underground. When the electric supply industry was nationalised, all further additions were made by overhead wires. On a later occasion I had the pleasure of temporarily shocking the complacency out of my fellow directors on the board of 'Eastern Electricity' by reminding them of this example of a lowering of standards after nationalisation.

There was also about as many unemployed then as in the late 1970s, but with the profound difference that in those pre-Keynsian days this was not accompanied by inflation. On the contrary, prices became lower and lower, and because the welfare state had not yet emerged there was a genuine interest in finding a job. The apparent paradox of today's high employment, combined with a difficulty in recruiting staff, did not exist.

Industry was not overtaxed and the principle that a government should do all that it could not to impose taxation unrelated to profits was well understood. Industry was 'derated' and this was a great help to young and struggling enterprises.

In fact, without any understanding of economics or realisation of what the future was to bring, I had by luck chosen an ideal time to start a new business. Naturally this was not the view of those who only saw the depressed state of industry; in particular Farren told me I had made a mistake, but then he was a man who spent his life giving other people 'good advice'. My father once retorted Oscar Wilde's advice to me, 'All advice is bad and good advice is fatal'; meaning people who give 'good advice' are bound to be over cautious and no outsider can understand a complicated personal position.

So now, as well as a scientist, I found I had become a 'man of affairs'.

The first objective was to make Aero Research Ltd known. Happily I was on good terms with the technical press, especially C. G. Grey, controversial editor of *The Aeroplane*. I wrote a number of articles such as the following:

Aeroplane – 6 June 1934, 'Plywood Construction for Aeroplanes'
Aircraft Engineering – February 1935, 'Bolted Joints in Wood'
Aeroplane – 27 November 1935, with K. Kenney, 'Ridigity of a Box Fuselage'
Aircraft Engineering – 1936, with J. N. Maas, 'A Property of Synthetic Resins'
Aeroplane – 19 February 1936, 'Improving the Creep Stress of Plastics'
Journal Royal Aeronautical Society – 1937, 'Plastic Materials for *Aircraft Construction*'. (The Simms Gold Medal was awarded me for this paper.)

Then a miracle happened. C. G. Walker, chief engineer of the de Havilland Aircraft Company, Ltd and F. T. Hearle, brother-in-law of G. de Havilland and managing director of the de Havilland Aircraft Company Ltd, after a short correspondence visited me at Trinity College. I remember giving them tea and having a walk round King's, Clare etc. They told me that de Havilland had seen my article in *Aeroplane* (6 June 1934) and had come to ask if I would act as consultant to investigate the possibilities of reinforced phenol formaldehyde resins for air screws. The outcome was a visit from me to Hatfield on 9 April 1936, from which I returned with a cheque for £1000 in my hand. I wonder whether de Havilland, in giving me that cheque, thought of the beginnings of his own enterprise in 1908 when he obtained £1000 from his grandfather and with his brother-in-law F. T. Hearle started to make his first aeroplane. As I drove back the heavens opened wide to reveal a chorus and trumpets making Handel-like noises. Anyway, it was a most understanding action on his part and I presented it next day with a grin to the bank manager, who had shown signs of restiveness with my financial position. A bank manager is like a man who loans you his umbrella when the sun is out but gets worried if it starts to rain; but if I were a bank manager no doubt I would behave in exactly the same way. Aero Research Ltd was opened officially on 3 October 1936, a pleasant autumn day, by D. T. Pye, deputy director of scientific research at the Air Ministry and a former Fellow of Trinity College (*The Times* 5 Oct 1936).

My feelings of joy were similar I imagine to that of an artist who has just sold his or her first picture. I felt I was being taken seriously, no longer just a schoolboy; I was impressed with the quality of the men I would be working with. My impressions were so exactly like those of O. W. H. Cooke, that I cannot do better than quote his words:

> My first impression was of the unaffected approachability of each and all of theses 'big shots' from 'DH' downwards. Here, it seemed, was a common sincerity of purpose and a total absence of mystery-making, backbiting, and money grabbing. There was a worthwhile job to do and we had the brains and resources to do it: very well then, let's get on with it, and the rewards will come along – at any rate that is the feeling that I got as a newcomer, and the one which stayed with me throughout my time. And I think this spirit of frankness and cordiality was the inspiration of that loyalty which is so evident.[28]

Mr Cooke is, of course, describing the de Havilland Aircraft Company of the days when it was still at Stag Lane. I spent the summer of 1931 there on a course (part of their apprenticeship scheme) for aeroplane owners. The same spirit was much in evidence at Hatfield.

Every Friday afternoon I visited C. C. Walker. He was an outstanding clear scientific thinker penetratingly interested in every manifestation of nature, unemotionally objective, and a man of utter integrity. He was also an inspiring and guileless humanitarian, exceptionally kind and humorous, and a leader in a curiously self-effacing way.

C. C. Walker's greatness was the product of a kind of subconscious synthesis of many qualities, technical and personal. Rich human qualities radiated from him and were felt by all who met

28. O. W. H. Cooke, 'Stag Lane and All That', *Aeroplane* 26 August 1960, pp. 252–3.

him, but perhaps of his technical attributes, the most important was his inquiring mind. It is interesting that he advocated a good working knowledge of physics as part and parcel of the education of people in almost any walk of life.

A close bond of friendship, despite a considerable difference in age, existed between myself and Mr Walker. On Mr Walker's death I wrote, 'All his life CCW was a source of strength to other people, his old age set a pattern I will try to follow. There was no "generation gap" with him, one felt completely at ease and his interest in everything was spontaneous and utterly genuine. I doubt if I shall ever meet a greater man.'

To give some idea of the wide interests of CCW's mind I reproduce below the substance of a letter I received from him on 3 September 1968: he died on 30 September 1968 aged 91 years.

> You very kindly sent me a paper by Michael Polanyi on a subject you knew was of great interest to me. My sight has been getting rather bad and when I tried to read this I found that the physical effort of deciphering the print drove out any power of concentration or comprehension, so that I found on this very interesting subject that I had no idea whatever of what he was saying. After one or two more efforts I got improved optical and illuminating aids, and the whole subject revealed itself like pulling up the curtains in a dark room. It is by far the best discussion on these subjects which I have ever seen, by a really qualified man. It sweeps away all the false bases for speculation and indicates clearly the probable avenue for speculators to go along. I quote the last paragraph in case you do not want me to return the paper, which shows the modesty of his claim relating to the mysterious and almost magical differences between inanimate and animate nature and its laws.
>
> The recognition of certain basic impossibilities had laid the foundations of some major principles of physics and chemistry; similarly recognition of the impossibility of understanding living things in terms of physics and chemistry, far from setting limits to our understanding of life, will guide it in the right direction. And even if the demonstration of this impossibility should prove of no great advantage in the pursuit of discovery, such a demonstration would help to draw a truer image of life and man than that given us by the present basic concepts of biology.
>
> I'm afraid you are in for rather a long letter, which is always rather

a curse to a busy man, but I rely on your having a reliable and working waste paper basket.

I have also read an article by John Kendrew FRS (Peterhouse) reviewing the work of Haldane and Bernal on the Origin of Life. I get the impression that Kendrew has his own reservations about work on these lines, which has always seemed to me very unsatisfactory. (Who am I to say this and why do I say it?) All these efforts other than Polanyi's seem to want it both ways. They want to find how this almost magical transition from dead to living things could occur spontaneously within their framework of universal degradation and decay. Many people seem to think that in a random series every conceivable combination must occur if you go on long enough, e.g. Thomas Huxley and his monkeys and typewriters. By continual uninformed bashing of the keys producing a Shakespeare sonnet given time enough. I think we can tell, you and I, that this is utter nonsense, random arrangements stay random however long you go on for and never get into any organised pattern. When people say 'ah, but you've not had enough experience, if you've lived for five hundred thousand years you might be qualified to say something about it', the answer to that is that one is able to look in on processes which have been going on for very much longer than that. Say, the gradual deposition in calm waters of fine sediments which rain down to the sea bed for thousands or millions of years on end. You don't find that they have formed, say, a bust of Winston Churchill, or anything else organised or complex. The slates, shales, chalk et cetera all possess a structure of what might be called maximum entropy, a random process never produces complex structures, its results are always higgledy piggledy, so I don't see how the exponents, other than Polanyi, can explore this question of creation of living things within the framework made by the second law and other spontaneous operations of dead matter. I will send you Kendrew's article under separate cover which I don't want back.

Yours

CCW

The original interest of the de Havilland Company in reinforced plastics was the possibility of using them in variable pitch propellers and in cooperation with the Bakelite Company (of England), they were exploring cotton cord reinforcement (as used in motor tyres) impregnated with a solution of phenol fomaldehyde resin.

The attraction of the reinforced plastic was that its density was about one half that of aluminium alloy so that the centrifugal force at the root end was correspondingly reduced. I purchased four inexpensive second hand hydraulic presses from George Cohen & Company and stood them in line on the floor at Duxford to produce a platen area big enough to press a reinforced stepped bakelite blank which could be afterwards machined to the correct shape in the same was as a wooden blade.

However, I was unsuccessful in producing a uniformly cured block of material because of its considerable thickness, and the project was dropped.

I was interested in producing a stronger reinforced material for aircraft construction and on the suggestion of Mr Gordon, an undergraduate at Trinity College, I tried flax as reinforcement. This produced a remarkably strong material which we called Gordon Aerolite with a specific gravity just about half of that of duralumin. With unidirectional reinforcements, the ultimate tensile strength was 70,000 Ib/sq in (482.3 x 10_6 pascals.) Young's modulus 7.0X10_6 Ib/sq in (482,300 x 10_6 pascals.) Density 85 Ib/cu ft (sq gravity 1.36.) With crossed reinforcement, a sheet material is produced with approximately equal strength and stiffness along and across the grain (as in plywood.) The Royal Aircraft Establishment report stated: 'it is considered that this material is the most promising organic sheet material yet produced for stressed skin covering for aircraft and it appears probable that, if available in quantity, it could be used directly to replace duralumin sheet in existing designs.' (RAE reference no. MT 56442.)

It may be asked why I did not use glass fibre and the following extract from Rayner's booklet is relevant:

> The pioneer nature of this work can be seen from an interchange of letters between Aero Research and the suppliers of glass fibre, which at that time was not made in England. A letter from Aero Research dated January 12, 1937 (the copy shows that 'DB' was then still typing his own letters), said:
>
> 'We are very interested in fabric made from glass 'silk'. We are interested in using it as a filler for synthetic resins, and we imagine it would have a high elastic modulus....'
>
> The reply was:

> the ordinary sense sold, it did in one form or another provide the company with further research contracts. One contract was for making thirty Miles 'Magister' tail planes, another was for a 'Spitfire' fuselage, all work of considerable importance at a time when a shortage of aluminium was a national problem.[29]

The construction of the 'Spitfire' fuselage has been described in *Aircraft Production*, July 1945, p. 323.

To get the flax fibres laid parallel to one another, we used a machine originally devised for making material for hats from ramie fiber. This was made to order by a small firm in Waldshut on the edge of the Black Forest and I remember with pleasure my walk with rucksack from Freiburg to Walshut to place the order.

In 1936 we decided that Aero Research Ltd would have to go into some kind of manufacturing that would not clash with its consulting and research work for outside firms. I thought that it would stabilise its financial position if instead of living entirely on our wits we had a steady pot boiling business of some kind. Like most dons I thought that 'business' must be much easier than solving research problems and in a way it is, but it calls for qualities and muscle not used in laboratory work.

Dr A. H. Wilson, also a Fellow of Trinity, and who later became chairman of Courtaulds Ltd, once remarked to me that of all industries the one that seemed to him to have the most potential for growth was the chemical industry. My experience with glues available at that time suggested that this might be a good line to follow.

I sent a letter dated 3 March 1937 to Robert Lea headed 'glue'.

> Dear Robert
>
> I have come to a decision – we must make the stuff ourselves. So I have collected a number of things to do it in a small way at first – 50 lbs a day. We start putting them together next week and will be operating the week after d.v. This will enable us to meet emergencies. It does not preclude us buying the stuff from I.C.I. as well.
>
> The total cost will only be £30 or so and I have a ton of urea and formaldehyde in stock to be used up and already paid for. We made 5 Lbs, as an experiment outfit, of what looks like good stuff yesterday. Am very busy – so are you!
>
> Yours ever

29. C. A. A. Rayner, *Milestones in the History of CIBA (A.R.L.) Limited (1934–59)*, Cambridge 1959.

'...I have to say that we see no prospect of glass 'silk' being suitable for moulded plastics.

'The elongation before fracture under tension is relatively small for such a purpose, and while we should only be very pleased to supply for any of the purposes for which Glass Silk is known to be suitable, you will, we feel sure, appreciate our reluctance to supply it for any purpose where it is possibly going to be a failure ....'

With scientific developments it is often difficult to discover who first set the ball rolling, and that is so with glass fibre. However, it appears that one of the first people to draw attention to its high tensile strength was A. A. Griffith (then of the Royal Aircraft Establishment) in a paper read before the Royal Society in 1920, entitled 'The Phenomena of Rupture and Flow in Solids'. The table below is taken from his paper.

Strength of glass fibres

Diameter in thousands of an inch	Breaking stress lb/sq. in
4.20	42,000
1.75	82,600
0.75	134,000
0.60	185,000
0.38	232,000
0.16	498,000

A Warren beam type of construction was designed for the spar, a design that necessitated considerable ingenuity where the making of joints was concerned because there were no suitable glues at that time, and the wood-like structure of 'Gordon Aerolite' meant that gluing was the ideal way of joining it.

Finally, it was decided to use a ring and groove type of mechanical joint. This type of joint follows the pattern of a correctly made glued joint, in that it subjects the material to a shear stress. It is, however, much more trouble to make, and it sacrifices material from where it cannot really be pared.

'Gordon Aerolite' was an important influence in the growth of Aero Research. It provided the financial foundation on which the company slowly grew through the difficult times of the late nineteen thirties and the first two or three years of the war, when 'Aerolite' glue was not paying its way. Although 'Gordon Aerolite' was not in

'The first stage up from the litre flask was a galvanised iron pot situated on the building seen in the photograph on the right (see Plate 9).

> Before being superseded by a copper pilot plant, this pot served a lot of valuable experiments, and generally taught us how not to do things. Steam for it was supplied by a small vertical boiler whose flue pipe you can see (in the photograph). This laundry boiler was brought for £10 delivered. Its maximum working pressure was only 7Ib a square inch, but there seemed to be no harm in weighting the release valve in order to obtain a little more. Never could this rather precious boiler be left unattended for long, and so it was no uncommon sight at lunchtime to see one or other of the staff, often A. Touhey (Bunt), F. Bird or C. Earey, standing by, a sandwich in one hand and a poker in the other. These versatile young men did a variety of jobs in connection with 'Aerolite' glue: they assisted with the experiment work in the laboratory, made the glue on the pilot plant, and packed and loaded it for dispatch. Bunt Touhey also turned out to be an excellent chemical plant plumber, in days when doing it yourself was the rule. [30]

We still wondered whether it might not be better to get 'Aerolite' glue made for us rather than get involved in the eventual capital expenditure and expense of manufacture on a large scale at Duxford; in our innocence we approached ICI who made UF moulding powders. We asked for a quotation and had several discussions and they gave a verbal undertaking not to compete with us. However, at the Royal Aeronautical Society annual reception on 27 January 1938, they exhibited samples of UF glue and hardener as their own. So, we broke off our relations rather abruptly. Commenting on this, Robert Lea in a letter dated 10 November 1978, wrote,

> 'here and there I remember a thing with a astonishing clarity, I remember for instance a 'fireside chat' at ICI in their offices ... The senior man said he was sorry things had gone wrong to which you replied, 'I have heard enough to know that you have behaved not only with duplicity, but with downright dishonesty'. Strong Stuff!

The years 1937 and 1938 were of great significance to the future of Aero Research Ltd. It was in 1937 that Robert R. G. Lea and

30. Ibid.

Claude A. A. Rayner joined us. Robert Lea was at Lancing and left a year after I did. He went to Clare College Cambridge. Robert wrote:

> We didn't really meet again until 1936, when I visited him at Trinity. I was working in the city and this was just a Sunday outing. Some outing for me. He showed me the very early beginnings of Aero Research Ltd at Duxford, and after a cup of tea I left him. The next day, Monday, I received a postcard saying, 'Why don't you join me?

Claude Rayner came to my office at Trinity in reply to an advertisement in the local paper. He did not write, he came. I pointed out all the disadvantages of joining ARL and that I was really looking for a lad and that he ought to have a further think and come back later, but he replied, 'As far as I am concerned, I have made up my mind.' So that was that.

> Boldness, in spite of troubles, saw Aerolite glue exhibited at the Royal Aeronautical Society's Garden Party in May 1937. The static exhibition was held in the original Heath Row hanger which today stands rather incongruously in the middle of London Airport. At this time the name 'Aerolite Cement' was used, a description that was gradually dropped during the following year or two, only to be revived when 'Redux' was developed. The difference of opinion over the relative merits of the names 'glue' and 'cement' still continues. Some consider the name 'cement' suggests greater permanence than 'glue', while others point out that cement itself it not really an adhesive.
>
> DB referred to the exhibiting of 'Aerolite' glue as its coming-out party, as indeed it was. On April 22, 1937, it had been given approval for use in aircraft, an approval given by the Air Ministry on the results of a series of tests made by a well-known firm of propeller manufacturers – the Airscrew Company, of Weybridge.
>
> Both 'Aerolite' glue and 'Gordon Aerolite' created a lot of interest at the R Ae.s Garden Party. Many questions were asked about their properties and today it must be confessed that many of the answers were not then known. A member of the staff recalls hearing Robert Lea in conversation with some flying-boat people: 'Does it stand sea-water?' 'Rather – loves it'. Does the toredo worm go for it?' 'What? – Oh, no, absolutely not – hates it'. Looking back it would seem that intelligent guesswork supplied many correct answers. Pirani, famous for the Pirani gauge and the tantalem metal filament lamp, on a visit to Duxford many years ago, remarked that, 'The trouble in answer-

ing questions about all new developments is that you are expected to know in advance the answers to problems you will still be working on twenty years later.'

In 1938, as a result of the interest aroused by the outstanding properties of 'Gordon Aerolite', Aero Research was given a contract by the Air Ministry for further developing it, in particular, for construction of a full-scale wing spar for a Bristol 'Blenheim' bomber. The award of this research contract was of great importance to the company, not only for its recognition of scientific achievements, but also for the financial relief that it brought. Up to this time, the financial affairs of the company were a continual source of anxiety. Here, a word or two about the money side will not be out of place. The company's registered capital was £100 in £1 shares, ninety-nine in the name Norman de Bruyne and one in the name of Pieter de Bruyne, his father. Its income came from two sources: first from DB's position as Junior Bursar of Trinity College, secondly from a research fee from the de Havilland Aircraft Company. And the first thing looked for in the mail on the first of the month was the arrival of de Havilland's cheque. So it is not surprising that when the Air Ministry contract was received there were feelings of relief – and a rise in pay all round. In the negotiation and subsequent supervision of this contract, the Deputy Director of Scientific Research of the Air Ministry, Mr W. S. Farren, played a material part. To Sir William for his forthright approach and to the Director of Scientific Research, Dr D. R. Pye, for his sympathetic understanding, Aero Research owes much.

The Bristol 'Blenheim' spar was a valuable exercise. Its construction required a special press of unusual design. Up to the time of starting work on the spar, the largest piece of 'Gordon Aerolite' ever made was 8 in. long, so the magnitude of the problems associated with designing and building a wing spar 30 ft long was large indeed. But courage was never lacking in those days when everyone was young. Today a more cautious spirit prevails. R. F. G. Lea, Commercial Director, reflecting on this recently, declared that although with middle age you keep a cooler head, you also get cold feet more easily. [31]

My time in 1937 was fairly well occupied as the following extracts from a memo to the Council of Trinity College confirm:

'The de Havilland Aircraft Company Ltd propose that I be at Hatfield on two afternoons a week ... I have consulted Prof. Inglis who said he was pleased that I should do this work.

31. Ibid.

12. Bobby Marsh, chief engineer, Aero Research Ltd, 1950s.

13. On the new Aerolite plant.

14. Bunt Toohey supervising the first bulk delivery of Aerolite resin.

15. Mould of one of four flaps for Boeing 777

16. Glue drums waiting to be stored in the newly built factory, Duxford, 1950.

17. The technology of synthetic resin adhesives, summer school 1951. Left to right: Mr F. H. Parker (Fairey Aviation Ltd), who lectured on the process used in bonding metals. Mr G. S. Newell (Aero Research Ltd) is holding the brake liner and next to him are Dr G. Sanderson Learmonth (Gandy Ltd) who described the bonding of brake linings, and Mr R. A. Johnson (Aero Research Ltd).

My hours at the Engineering Labs are confined to mornings; my lectures are from 11 – 12 on Wednesdays and Saturdays and demonstrations from 9 – 11 on three days a week.

The de Havilland works are at Hatfield and are about an hour's run in a car. I would leave Cambridge at 1.0 pm and return by 6.30 pm.

And then until 8.0 pm I had 'supervision' (private tuition) to give in my rooms at Trinity.'

The memo concludes:

'I do not think that the changes proposed will diminish the time I can give to my college duties or put any additional burden on me and I hope that I may be able to be more productive than I can be at present.'

(The year 1938) started off with the award of the research contract for the Bristol 'Blenheim' spar. Later on a new office building was completed; the original hanger was extended and a new one built. A mechanically-fired hot water system was installed, solving for ever the early morning problem of who should light the boiler – if it had gone out, and it frequently had. Then on 19 June 1938, a second-hand aeroplane arrived – a Desoutter monoplane, made in 1929, bought for £100 by 'DB' and his brother Bernard without a C. of A. 'DB' gingerly flew it over from Gloucester. George Newell tells of the reek of sour milk in the fuselage, and of the clouds of mould spores filling the air when the half-delaminated plywood was ripped off. This aeroplane probably made history. It may well have been the first in England to use a synthetic resin assembly glue because in the construction of what was a substantially rebuilt wooden fuselage 'Aerolite' glue was used throughout. It was also in the reconstruction of this fuselage with its plywood skin that we ourselves experienced the effect known as case-hardening.[32]

Case-hardening, produced on the surface of plywood, results in the plywood being 'unglueable'.It was first brought to our attention in November 1937 by Mr Marcus Langley, at that time Chief Designer of the British Aircraft Manufacturing Co Ltd, of Feltham. We retested his consignment of 'Aerolite' glue and found it met specification 4V3 but joints made with samples of the particular plywood used showed poor adhesion. We tried various remedies without success but on 25 November 1937, the following entry occurs in Rayner's notebook: 'Surface (of ply) glass-papered almost

32. Ibid.

down to Tego glue film but still leaving an unbroken surface of wood; adhesion very good, one or two laminations adherent over entire length of test specimens.' By comparison with untreated controls this established that the poor adhesion was a surface effect, was not due to contamination by the plywood adhesive, and suggested a remedy, without giving much of a clue to the cause of the trouble.

When repairing the plywood fuselage of the old Desoutter, we found that the new plywood was very difficult to stick to the spruce longerons and stiffeners. The ply could be stripped away, after the glue had set, without any signs of wood rupture. This personal experience emphasized the importance of the phenomenon and we felt it our duty in a letter dated 13th October 1938, to circulate the plywood manufacturers and to bring the matter to the attention of the Air Ministry and to the technical press (see Flight 28 December 1939). However, no official action was taken to make sanding along the grain mandatory until 1942, and in Bulletin 21 of the *Aero Research Technical Notes* (September 1944), I remarked, 'It is regrettable that it has needed actual loss of life to secure that general acceptance and the necessary preventative measures.'

> Also during the year 1938 a small second-hand paper-coating plant was purchased because work on the development of a urea resin film glue was considered to show promise.
>
> In Germany, a press of novel design and construction for making long lengths of 'Gordon Aerolite' in 'bites' was nearing completion. Then came Munich. War or threat of war notwithstanding, this press had to be got to Duxford. While Chamberlain conferred with Hitler at Bad Godesberg, DB flew off to Dusseldorf and arranged for the makers to deliver the press, untested and unassembled, to mutual friends in Holland; but such steps were, of course, not necessary and the press arrived a month later.
>
> In September 1937 DB, while remaining a Fellow of Trinity College, resigned his Bursarship to take a post as College Lecturer and University Demonstrator in Mechanical Sciences enabling him to spend more time at Duxford, driving out daily in his Austin Seven. The year 1938 closed with the staff having grown from four to ten.' [33]

In 1939, Donald A Hubbard (1916-78) came to us to take charge of Urea Formaldehyde production. He had been trained at Nottingham as a pharmaceutical chemist but found it too petty a

33. Ibid.

job to his liking. At Aero Research he took over the entire management of 'Aerolite' glue production when Claud Rayner left to join the Fleet Air Arm. With Dr Daphne Bamford a test was established which permitted the operator to follow the degree of condensation of the UF resin and for the first time made it possible to produce a consistent product with predictable properties.

> Nineteen thirty-nine saw the completion of a three-storey building, containing the first real production size plant for Aerolite glue.
>
> No sooner had it started than it came very near to being stopped by an Excise Inspector visiting the factory to approve a store for methylated spirits. Taken on a short cut through the plant by a member of the staff, he stopped to inquire if those things were stills. With naive enthusiasm he was told, 'Oh yes, they are in a way.'
>
> The construction of the 'Blenheim' spar was finished and work was started on Miles 'Magister' tailplanes in reinforced plastic materials. The rational design and construction of these tailplanes was handicapped by lack of a suitable glue; all the same, they were stronger than their wooden counterparts and weighed less.
>
> During the research on urea resins an important observation was made which led to the company being the only one to supply a separate-application gapfilling hardener. This observation was related to the behaviour of urea resins on addition of formic acid, and from it were developed the well-known GB range of hardeners.
>
> The war came with its gas masks and blackout, and on the first night, the works were broken into. Many were the colourful stories that went around the village – at a time when the people still wondered what they did 'up at the Research'. But the thief only went off with the petty cash and a suit left behind by Robert Lea when mobilised three days before. The burglary gave the company a feeling of increased importance: the buildings were camouflaged, a night watchman engaged.
>
> The landing ground was ploughed up and from that day to this, acre by acre, it is being taken back for extensions of one sort or another – buildings, roads, effluent disposal, games field.[34]

In the above extract from Rayner's booklet of 1959, he omits his own name as the discoverer of the unique properties of formic acid as a catalyst for UF resins. This was of great importance to the use of Aerolite UF glues in aircraft and boat construction as the properties of the cured glue were superior to those of UF glues with fillers and also enabled one to dispense with weighing out and mixing

34. Ibid.

catalyst and glue. The British Power Boat Company adopted 'Aerolite' on the basis of their own tests. Aerolite, in powder form with GB hardeners, became the only UF glue approved for use by the Royal Air Force.

In July 1939, I accompanied Arthur Marshall in his Stinson monoplane G-AFRS on a flight to Poland. We left Cambridge at 14.18 on 4 August and arrived at Berlin at 20.05 having stopped at Lympne. On Saturday 5 August we arrived at Danzig at 15.16 and Arthur asked the taxi driver whether there was going to be a war and got a firmly affirmative reply. We reached Warsaw at 12.15 on Sunday 6 August where I was amazed by the ghetto and the grass growing between the railway tracks at the main station. The obvious inadequacy of the military aircraft forced us to conclude that Germany could overrun the country in a few weeks. Hitler invaded Poland on 1 September, followed by Russian invasion on 17 September, and Warsaw surrendered on 27 September and on 29 September the partition of Poland was agreed between Germany and Russia.

On 1 December 1939, I was visited by Herman Lebus and his technical manager, Mr A. R. Lain. They came to learn about our 'strip heating' system which the setting of 'Aerolite' glue by the use of low voltage – high amperage currents in to steel strips applied to curved surfaces such as wings. I showed them everything. Lebus claimed to be the largest furniture manufacturer in the World. I later made an application, after the war, to the Royal Commission on Awards to Inventors for this invention which significantly increased the rate of production of gliders and Mosquito aeroplanes. I found when I got to the hearing in 1950, that the Ministry of Aircraft production opposed my claim on the grounds that Lebus had devised the process, and they encouraged Lebus to put in a counterclaim. Mr Lain, to do him justice, apologised to me after the proceedings – saying that it was Lebus who forced him to put in the claim. Strip heating was used by twenty-seven firms, mainly in the construction of de Havilland Mosquitoes, Horsa gliders and assault boats. With the same jigs and the same floor space, 'strip heating' enabled productivity of gluing operations to be increased by at least twenty times by decreasing the setting time of the glue from hours to minutes. Many millions of pounds worth of equipment was glued in this way and it is doubtful if it could have been produced in such quantity without it. I was awarded £1,000 by the

Commission and the lawyers took £800. With this experience in mind I withdrew my claim for 'Redux' and took legal proceedings against the Ministry instead. The Ministry's reaction was to deny that I was the inventor and they tried to get Dr M. G. M. Pryor and J. E. Gordon and others to sign a statement that it had been invented at the RAE at Farnborough which they refused.

> Shooting was taken seriously the next summer when a unit of the Home Guard was formed. And when a number of Dornier bombers flew over during the Battle of Britain, the Home Guard jumped into their more-or-less strategically placed trenches, to defend the factory against an enemy which was expected to parachute down on it every time the siren went.
>
> The year 1940 saw the close of the research association with de Havilland's. Busily occupied with the urgent problems presented by war, they saw in structural plastics a material too remote for immediate consideration. [35]

We continued, however, to work for the MAP (Ministry of Aircraft Production) though it became clear that the official view was that Aero Research Ltd, was an organisational anomaly and that all plastics research work should be concentrated in one place and should be completely separated from production. One suggestion was that some of the staff at RAE should be transferred to Duxford; Aero Research Ltd, would cease to make and sell glue. This was a suggestion to which I could not of course agree. Their next action was to insist that all future contracts should be at a fixed price; previously they had been 'cost plus' with a rigourous examination of all expenses and many disallowances (such as interest paid by Aero Research Ltd to the bank on its overdraft, and any allowance for profit.) I was told that the 'Spitfire' contract would have to be for a fixed price and the price I gave was accepted by the MAP. However, when their agents came to inspect our books, they found we had made a profit on the transaction and they withheld payment. When I refused to issue a credit note to cover the profit, all equipment including the special Siempelkamp press was removed to the PAE. A compromise was eventually reached with the MAP after I had written to our member of Parliament. So now I was on my Beam ends; but on the strength of my ground engineer's licence, I

35. Ibid.

asked Arthur Marshall if he had any aircraft repair work for me. Fortunately he had, and we began to repair Airspeed 'Oxfords'. The 'Oxford' was the RAF version of the 'Envoy' designed by Norway (Nevil Shute) and Tiltman of Airspeed and it was the standard twin engine training aircraft of the British Commonwealth during the war. It was an excellent wooden machine with a retractable undercarriage.

Nineteen forty-one was the year in which my brother-in-law, Robert Marsh, came to ARL as Chief Engineer. He took his degree in engineering at Cambridge and then went to the USA to work with William Emmet ('Uncle Bill') of the General Electric Company on the mercury boiler. This was an ingenious way of driving a turbine with mercury vapour which permitted one to obtain higher temperatures without the high pressure that steam would have. He then came back to the British Thomson Houston Company, which in those days was associated with the General Electric (USA), to work on turbine installations for ships. His works are to be seen all over the plant at Duxford; he and Donald Hubbard planned and installed the large UF plant and spray drier and he designed a host of ingenious equipment such as that for upending and filling drums automatically. He used back pressure steam to drive a turbine to grind the UF powder coming out of the spray drier.

F. B. Priest (later sales manager of Aerolite Division), a keen yachtsman, joined us on 7 March 1941 and became the first person to design and build an all-glued boat. The water proof qualities of Aerolite were put to good use by British Power Boats, but no one had made a 'moulded' shell without screws or nails. Frank Priest built a 9ft cold molded dinghy in his own time and completed it in 1942.

Perhaps as a relief from having officialdom off my back, I wrote a 'Note on Viscous and Plastic Flow',[36] based on J. C. Maxwell's concept of relaxation time and Kuhn's suggestion that liquids and solids have approximately the same shear modulus.

I am glad to say that the RAF carried on with the development of reinforced plastics though in my opinion they made a mistake in substituting asbestos for flax reinforcement. However, after the war they went over to the use of carbon fibre reinforcement and this changed the whole situation. It is interesting to read in Sir Frank

36. N. A. de Bruyne, 'Note on Viscous and Plastic Flow', *Proceedings of the Physical Society*, Vol. 53 (1941), p 251.

Whittle's autobiography *Jet* how he was treated by the same bureaucracy; and it does not show bureaucracy at its best.

Looking back I can see now that the withdrawal of the backing by the MAP though it was a calamity at the time, was in the long run beneficial. It gave me the freedom to develop Redux. With the appointment of Harry Lincoln who did a splendid job as works manager, I was able to keep clear of paper work.

In 1941, we had a fire in the sheds in which doping of aircraft fabric was carried out. The Desoutter GAPPU was completely destroyed though, fortunately, the Gipsy Major engine had been removed and stored in another building. The fire started while we were having our annual Christmas party at a hall in Duxford though I did not hear of it until I was just about to get into bed. It was quite a blaze and all that was left was a somewhat twisted steel framework.

Before the close association with de Havilland's came to an end, in a report dated May 20, 1941, entitled 'Notes on the Value of Light Materials for Struts and Shells', DB wrote: 'The final conclusion from these notes it that a balsa fuselage covered on both sides with "Duralumin" should be an extremely efficient structure. Its manufacture would only be possible if the problem of adhesion between balsa and 'Duralumin' were satisfactorily solved.'

Six months later came 'Redux', and it is an interesting fact that the use of 'Redux' in the Chance Vought 'Cutlass', a US Navy fighter under construction in the years 1952-7, was in just that application – sticking 'Duralumin' to a balsa core. But credit must go to Chance Vought for employing the balsa in a more efficient manner, with its grain perpendicular to the skin.

The work on metal adhesives had been directed first and foremost towards use in the construction of metal aircraft. Nevertheless, the first practical application of 'Redux' was not in aeroplanes but in tanks – in bonding several thousand clutches from Cromwell and Churchill tanks, giving a life of between two and three thousand miles compared with two hundred for riveted clutches.

In 1940, permission to build a new laboratory had been granted and this was completed in 1941, releasing the bungalow laboratory for other use. This bungalow inside the grounds of Aero Research is a notable feature of our landscape, and a frequent cause for comment by visitors. It began life in 1936 as a standard Boulton and Paul prefabricated bungalow, perched on a flat roof and used by DB and others as a casual home. In 1938, it became the chemical research labo-

> ratory. In 1944, it was re-erected at ground level and become successively the home of two members of the staff. In 1953, it was made into a drawing office, and today it is the coveted office of the Works Director.[37]

In 1942, we went over to the repair of wings of Short 'Stirling' bombers under a subcontract from Short Bros. who had a 'shadow factory' in Cambridge.

We exhibited a Redux-bonded aluminium alloy compression panel at an exhibition organized by the Society of British Aircraft Constructors at the Grosvenor House Hotel in London in 1942. We also had on our stand a pile of lap joints which we invited people to break. Of course, no one could. R. E. Bishop, chief designer of the de Havilland Company, came to this exhibition and as a result used Redux in the 'Hornet', which was the fastest propeller driven machine ever made. When the 'Mosquito' and the 'Hornet' had to be fitted with folding wings for naval use, Redux was used for the hinge joints. For further information about the history of Redux, see Appendix 3.

In 1943, for the first time, the glue department made a profit largely due to the construction of Horsa gliders using Aerolite 300 and GB hardeners by Morris Motors using strip heating. Of course, Excess profits Tax (EPT) took the whole amount of profit as we had no profits before the war. We were lucky to be in business but I could not help being annoyed that the banks and breweries and many others, merely because they had made large profits before the war, were immune from EPT. It was indeed a 'tax on enterprise growth and youth' to quote Keynes's words about a similar post war tax. We were allowed to make a gross profit of £3,500 a year less income tax giving a net profit of £1,750 a year which was absorbed by director's remuneration and other non tax deductible expenses. However, there was a considerable lag between making a profit and having to pay tax so that as long as one continued to make profits one had additional capital available and so I purchased a steel framed building from a site in Wales, a spray drier from a man who had been put out of business by illegally (i.e. without government permission) obtaining corn starch to make noodles, and a large copper reaction vessel. But we were still in difficulties in getting enough

37. C. A. A. Rayner, *Milestones in the History of CIBA (A.R.L.) Limited (1934–59)*, Cambridge 1959.

cash and at this juncture Robert Lea lent us £2,000 without security at a rate of six per cent. The National Provincial Bank Ltd (now the National Westminster Bank), agreed to an increased overdraft provided I pledged everything I possessed (including my home) as security, which I did.

> Sometimes separately, sometimes together, Donald Hubbard and DB travelled the country to interest people in 'Aerolite' glue. The military glider programme created a valuable market. D. A. Hubbard at the same time looked after glue production and managed to find time for research on the glues as well. Control methods were devised which led to Aerolite becoming acknowledged as foremost in batch-to-batch consistency.
>
> The output of the first production plant was now too small, a second plant was installed in a more conveniently arranged building and this was completed in 1943. Pending the delivery of a new boiler, there was now a temporary shortage of steam, which was alleviated by two John Fowler steam engines; (similar to the Fowler ploughing engines sold in Victorian times by Max Eyth and described in *Hinter Pflug und Schraubstock*. (Deutsche Verlags – Anstalt, Stuttgart 1958); and the story goes that they were used alternately, one under a corrugated iron awning on wet days and the other out in the open when it was fine.
>
> In 1944 Aerodux 184, the first resorcinol resin to be produced in the country, was put on the market. Later it was superseded by 'Aerodux' 185, a glue that is used today in increasing amounts, particularly in the construction of laminated beams.[38]

R. J. Fawcett came to us in 1944, straight from Price Waterhouse, who were our auditors, to become secretary of the Company. He brought a new detached professional outlook to the consideration of our affairs and everyone respected him. At one time he was also personnel officer. He was educated at Rugby and then went to Cambridge.

Robert Lea, who returned in September 1945, took charge of our sales with F. B. Priest as office manager for 'Aerolite', C. J. Moss in charge of Redux, Dr Israel Burzstyn in charge of resins for paper, and D. A. Hubbard in charge of production. In a letter to Lea dated 30 August 1945, I wrote:

38. Ibid.

The man with whom you will have most to do is D. A. Hubbard. He came just after you left and it is no exaggeration to say that the glue business is his creation on the technical side making use admittedly of Rayner's instruction and of Rayner's discovery of the magical properties of formic acid as a hardener. Hubbard kept on despite all discouragement and he rightly feels that Aerolite glue as a viable business, is very much his baby. He is at the present time in charge of production, but delegates most of the work to H. S. Bannister and spends most of his time selling glue and radio heating sets. You will, however, be heartened to observe that our best customers remain the ones you got.

The chief changes since your day in that we are now 100 per cent all out for 'separate application'. . . this is where we have made all the profits. Fawcett has got the costing side thoroughly covered and he will be a great help to you. I think one section of sales you might make your own speciality, is 'EXPORT'.

One thing was clear: for the company to remain in business producing synthetic glues it must export. Moreover, it must export quickly in order to tide it over the period while industrial reshuffling was taking place at home. In September 1945, Robert Lea returned from the Royal Air Force and straightaway packed his bags for Sweden. Leaving D. A. Hubbard there, he managed to get into Finland without a visa and sent a cable 'Have sold 100 tons.' Then he found the Swedish police waiting for him, and spent a day under arrest while trying to raise enough money to pay the fine. That was only the start of the export business. Then urea was rationed.

In the first two or three years of peace, special efforts were made to create new markets for 'Aerolite' glues in applications outside the gluing of wood, particularly for wet-strengthening paper, and as a binder in foundry sand cores. The former had every appearance of developing into a big market; before long every housewife would insist on a wet-strength paper bag for her tomatoes and grapes (a thing she has yet to do.) A valuable outlet was however found in photographic paper. . .

We could clearly expect to sell more glue abroad, especially in Australia, New Zealand, Africa, India, Finland, Holland, Belgium, and in S. America. As time went on it was realised that the demand for 'Aerolite' glue would before long outstrip the company's capacity to make it. Then, as now, the maxim was that production must be ahead of demand, a policy that has so far as possible always been put into practice, and one that has received the wholehearted support of CIBA.

The growing exports meant more output from one rather small

> spray dryer; it was squeezed to the limit. The cost of a new and larger one was £30,000 – it could not be done. [39]

I visited Germany with the very temporary rank of Lt Colonel on 21 November 1945, as a one-man 'reparation assessment team', and visited the former I G Farben Industrie factories at Leverkusen, Troisdork and Krefeld and the Henkel factory at Dusseldorf, all of which were in the British zone. Then I went south to the BASF at Ludwigshafen and Hoechst, but spent the nights at Heidelberg in the US zone. There were rumours that the Germans had produced a polyurethane metal-to-metal adhesive for aircraft during the war. I was also interested to see how they were making 'Kaurit'. I wrote up my findings which were published. This trip to Germany made me realise the scale of the industry which we had entered and the importance of making our own formaldehyde. It was clear that we had to raise considerable capital. In the four years preceding that trip I had spent a lot of time and energy trying to get financial backing. The predominant position of ICI was nearly always quoted against us in these discussions; on one occasion we were told that it would be hopeless for us to try to compete with ICI in the adhesive field so long as it monopolised the control of urea. On two other occasions, it was put to us by the people with whom we were negotiating that their principals were on good terms with ICI or knew important directors personally; the inference being that to stand well with the ICI was a business asset. It was little use to emphasise our technical superiority as evidenced by our 'Aero Research Technical Notes' which we knew were studied and used by the ICI salesmen, by our introduction of microwave heating, our specialised instruments such as the gelation timer, our gap filling glues, aircraft glues, strip heating, strong composite materials etc.

The supply of our raw materials was controlled by Ministry of Supply Plastics Control and by the Ministry of Aircraft Production. They were staffed by persons drawn from the plastics industry. They did a good job so far as the senior staff were concerned but less good at the lower levels as evidenced by the extract below from a letter from one of our customers.

39. Ibid.

I received a telephone message from a Mr. . . to the effect that in the national interest my application for two tons of glue would be limited to one only. In the course of conversation I was asked why our firm was using Aerolite. I stated that my position as secretary gave me no control over the decisions made by those in authority, but made it clear that complete satisfaction had been obtained by those concerned just in its use. He then mentioned that with such a wide range of glues to choose from, he was surprised we had selected your product and suggested that similar glues made by ICI would suit our purpose equally well.'

CHAPTER NINE

CIBA (ARL) LTD

MY first contact with CIBA (The Society of Chemical Industry, Basle) had been made in the early days of the war, when we had successfully obtained a licence from (I think) the custodian of enemy property to use Henkel's melamine formaldehyde patent. Soon after I received a visit from Dr Braendle (who later became secretary to the board of CIBA) and he offered me a licence from CIBA in place of the compulsory licence from Henkel with the advantage of technical assistance from CIBA. Dr Braendle made a very good impression on me and when in 1947 I was visited by Dr Engi of CIBA, who had come to withdraw the licence from Aero Research Ltd, I felt sufficiently at ease with CIBA to show without actually saying so that I would be happy to work with them. I remember that the late Robbie Fawcett, who was present during our discussions, was mystified by our discussions and said he could not understand what it was all about and that it seemed to be a waste of time leading to no conclusions. But an interview is an exchange of attitudes; it is a refined human equivalent of dog meeting dog. I sensed that Dr Engi was keenly interested in us and our little factory and sure enough Lea and I were soon after invited to Basle.

> The most momentous decision for the founder of any company to make is to part with it. With Aero Research it was difficult indeed. Here was an intimate organisation – full of growing pains but acquiring maturity – in which everyone knew everyone. That 'DB' found the decision difficult to make is understandable. In a similar situation on three previous occasions – during the war to make ends meet and afterwards to provide capital for expansion – he had withheld his signature at the last moment, on one notable occasion with the pen almost in his hand. Painful as the decision may have been, the wis-

> dom of it was unquestionable. To the company's employees it was one of far reaching significance.'[40]

I felt that I had at last got the ship round Cape Horn.

The board of directors included N. A. de Bruyne as managing director and R. F. G. Lea as commercial director with Raymond Needham QC as chairman. CIBA was represented on the board by Dr Robert Kappeli, chairman of the board of CIBA and Dr Karl Frey, head of plastics research. The name of the company was still Aero Research Ltd and it was not until 30 June 1958 that it was changed to CIBA (ARL) Ltd. Since 1970 it has been Ciba-Geigy (UK).

One day I picked up the telephone to tell the local authorities that we would be expanding and was greeted by a shrill voice, unmistakeably belonging to the wife of a Trinity College don saying, 'Where are you?' 'At Duxford.' 'You can't be, it is not an industrial development area!' 'We have been here for about ten years.' 'I shall have to make enquiries.' The new age of planning had arrived. The eventual outcome of the conversation was that we were told to move to Wigan (well known for its pier). Soon the local council began to build semi-detached houses in our vicinity; they were reserved for farm workers. At this point I wisely handed further negotiations over to Robert Lea. He asked me 'What do you want?' 'I want to stay here: it is an ideal site.'

He found that there was an OL (an old Lancing man) in the wartime temporary huts that housed officialdom in Brooklands Avenue, Cambridge. But it was uphill work and at one point even Robert Lea was heard to say, 'This will be the last factory to be built in England.'

Meanwhile the politicians of all parties bought votes by promises and actions which laid enormous burdens on industry. The spirit of the times is well reflected in Lord Butler's Memoirs *The Art of the Possible.* He knew that it was wrong to build 300,000 houses a year and to introduce an Excess Profits Levy, but nevertheless felt powerless to resist. What would Gladstone have said about that? Of the 300,000 houses he writes, 'Both the promise and the achievement were magnificent politically; economically however, they placed a severe inflationary strain upon our resources which contributed to the difficulties of 1954-5.' For the Excess Profits Levy he squarely

40. Ibid.

puts the blame on Churchill, who, in appointing him Chancellor of the Exchequer, said 'You will have to show good will by putting the Excess Profits Levy into force.'[41]

The effect of all this on our Swiss connection was not helpful. Hans Meiner remarked to me that 'if only' England had followed the German example where they built hotels for foreign buyers to get industry on its feet, then, when the economy could stand it, built houses. There was, however, still warm good will for England and belief that it could again be a great nation able to make its presence felt in Europe, and the question put to me by my Dutch cousins, 'What are you dear lunatics up to now?' had not yet ceased to be humorous.

Meanwhile we went ahead (as we did long ago with the Snark) in the conviction that given time and a good case one can always wear down a civil servant. And Robert Lea got permission for us to expand at Duxford and even more surprising was granted fifty to sixty prefabricated bungalows for our future employees. Hubbard recommended the firm of Ove Arup as architect and structural engineering consultants; and it certainly proved to be a good recommendation. The name of Arup to me signified reinforced concrete, but to my surprise we got a crystal palace of steelwork and glass; it was a tent over our chemical plant which included a giant spray drier and a big formalin plant. At night it looked beautiful.

When Dr Kappeli first saw it he was rather taken aback both by its size and by its structure. He asked whether 'Basle' had played any part in it; it seemed that 'Basle' built with nothing but concrete and we had found an entirely different solution. But he was pleased with what he had got for his money and the scale of operations which it portended; he had not, I think, visualised our production of plastics as being a heavy industry.

The new plant enabled us to reduce our prices drastically but we were still in the hands of ICI for our urea and methanol supplies.

OUR STRUGGLE WITH ICI

The duty on imported methanol, used for conversion to formaldehyde was 33 $^{1}/_{3}$ per cent and the only British maker was ICI The

41. R. A. B Butler, *The Art of the Possible*, Harmondsworth 1973.

result was that our UF glue could not compete with the German product in for example Finland where Robert Lea had penetrated immediately after his return from the RAF. We put this to the ICI and I received a letter reproduced below from the chairman, Mr Paul Chambers, a former civil servant in the Inland Revenue department, who had won fame and acclaim I am told in Civil Service circles for introducing the PAYE system which loaded on to industry a fair slice of the work of his department.

Imperial Chemical Industries Limited
Imperial Chemical House, Millbank
London, SW1

23 July 1959

Dear Dr de Bruyne,

When you visited me the other day with Dr Wilhelm you raised the question of the price at which we supplied methanol to Aero Research Limited of Duxford, Cambridge, and I promised to look into the matter.

I have found that the matter has been most carefully examined and re-examined over a very long period – and that the price which we charge you is exactly in line with what is charged for the same quantities to other customers. I am informed that we could make a price reduction of £1 per ton if you were prepared to enter into a five year contract, but that at the moment you were not inclined to do this.

The point raised by you or Dr Wilhelm was that perhaps we might consider a lower price for that quantity of methanol which you use to make products for export; because in your belief your competitors overseas have the advantage of lower methanol prices.

This has also been examined and I am sorry that it will not be possible to make any reduction in the price on this account.

May I say how sorry I am that this reply should be so negative, but I can assure you that we are most anxious to do all we can to help. Indeed, had it been possible to make any concession, I am sure that this would have been done on the basis of the evidence which you had already supplied and without troubling you to refer the matter to me.

With kind regards

Yours sincerely
Paul Chambers.

What the letter does not say, and to do justice to Mr Chambers what he may not have been told, is that ICI's equipment and process from making methanol were obsolete. There is a curious mistake in the letter; I never visited him. He probably confused me with Dr Brunner, the managing director of Clayton Aniline Company.

The next step clearly was to apply for abolition of the import duty. However, the Clayton Aniline Company (partly owned by CIBA) expressed concern that our actions might imperil their friendly relations with ICI and it was not until we obtained the approval of Dr Robert Kappeli, head of CIBA, that we felt able to proceed.

When we approached the Board of Trade we became acutely aware that the policy of its tariff and import policy division was protectionist and that it had to consult the Society of Chemical Manufacturers before making any move. Nevertheless we persisted and on 7 April 1960 the division issued a public notice stating that an application had been received for removal of import duty on methanol. On 26 may 1961 it refused our application but reduced the duty from 33 $^1/_3$ per cent to 27 per cent.

We found that even at 27 per cent it paid us to import methanol from the Gulf of Mexico (USA). The ICI salesman could hardly believe his ears when on his routine call he was informed that we did not want anything from him today, thank you. But we still could not regain the Finnish business with 27$^1/_2$ per cent duty to be paid.

ICI sales department invited us to a luxurious lunch and asked what our plans were. During our discussion I asked them why they needed such a heavy protection and it transpired that it was because they were using an obsolete process of manufacture based on coke instead of oil. Very noble expressions appeared on their faces as they explained that it was their duty to help the British Coal industry in the national interest. So the enormous McKenna duties imposed after World War I to assist firms such as ICI to build up their business were now necessary to protect their obsolete plant.

Our experience with ICI and with other chemical manufacturers such as Holliday (who had a monopoly of the manufacture of resorcinol) convinced me that a protectionist policy coupled with collusion between companies to fix prices as well as the encouragement of mergers ('rationalisation') was harmful to British industry. While

USA also had high import duties, it had strong 'Anti-Trust' laws which ensured that there was genuine competition. Capitalism without competition is almost as bad for a country's economic health as nationalisation. As Mr W. E. Nixon, managing director of the de Havilland Aircraft Company said at the conclusion of a colloquium organized by Professor Sir Ronald Edwards, 'The discussion showed once again that sheer largeness in an organization above a level of efficiency, is an enemy of success, also that monopoly is an enemy of success; and that largeness with monopoly is the arch enemy of success.'

Concerning competition, my friend Ronald Edwards gave an address shortly before his death which in my opinion is one of the best things he ever wrote. It was given to the 1975 conference of the European Research Management Association at Edinburgh and its theme is the need for competition.

> My case for competition does not rest on prejudice or on general impressions. It is based on personal observation and experience . . .
>
> My colleagues and I know that day by day other firms are working to improve the products they sell against our own, to strengthen the research teams, that – if successful – may put our major products out of business ... When we see a firm slipping, or a major product losing its market share in a competitive market, we know how desperately those concerned will, or should be, straining because we know what it would be like in our own organisation – If one takes one aspect of one part of my Group's activities namely research into pharmaceutical products ... you would think I find it hard to match the achievements of the big American, British, German, French and Swiss firms and indeed some of the smaller ones with anything of comparable significance in those societies that believe in close, central planning. It was a small group of young men who, in the Beecham Laboratories, isolated the penicillin nucleus which led subsequently to the creation of a large range of semi-synthetic penicillins which revolutionised the antibiotic business ... the chairman of the group, Lesile Lazell, was willing to plough back his firm's profits from other fields year after year . . . I have great doubt, and I say this as one who has worked in the public sector, whether, had the budget year by year, come before a highly intelligent and well informed Government Committee they would have recommended Beecham continuing the research to the stage at which it revolutionised the penicillin field. You may argue that I am wrong about this and that there are plenty of examples where Governments *have* continued

> projects for very long periods and achieved success – and even more projects supported for very long periods which have not achieved success. I can certainly think of some big ones myself. I think, however, there is something of a difference which scientists may find it a little difficult to accept. The difference is this. If you are in a University you carry on your research at your own speed. If you work for a University or a Government Department you know your job is safe. If, however, you work for a firm and know that either your research must be successful in producing products of processes that people want, otherwise the research will be cut down and your job will be at risk, I think the pressure is that much greater and the attitude that much different. The incentive is much greater when you know that others in your own country and across the world are under similar pressure in rivalry with you and that even if they have only a very short lead, they will be winners and you will be the losers.

The decline in the economic position of Britain did not begin after World War I (though it has accelerated since then) as the following quotations make clear.

'We can make our own iron, and our own tools. In fact instead of borrowing engines from abroad, we now send them to all parts of the world. British built ships ply on every sea. We export machinery to all countries and supply Holland itself with pumping engines.'[42]

> The trade of the world has increased; the share of the United Kingdom has decreased and is decreasing. It is decreasing in the world; it is decreasing in Europe and as we examine one group of industries after another the same phenomenon presents itself. It is due neither to inflation here, nor to deflation there, nor to poverty nor to tariffs. If high tariffs were the cause of our difficulties, they should have curtailed the trade of other nations more than ours.
> (A. Loveday, 1913)

Admittedly, England could not expect to be the world's workshop forever, but it should have been able to remain one of the world's leaders in technology. For this failure our class and educational system carries a heavy responsibility and to this must be added our laziness:

42. Samuel Smiles, *Lives of the Engineers,* 1867.

> The laziness of our race is often noticed by foreigners, and without much contradiction till the industrial revolution altered the habits of the people. In the nineteenth century, it is true, French observers reported that the English 'work fiercely'; but the older habits have now reasserted themselves, and it cannot be questioned that the average Englishman has no taste for the untiring, laborious diligence of the German. The slackness of the British workman excites the surprise and contempt of all foreign observers, especially of the Americans, who rightly see in it a ominous symptom of national deterioration. (Dean William Ralph Inge,1926)

An action which seemed right at the time but which has since had disastrous results was the concession by Parliament in 1906 to trade a view of the inviolability of their corporate funds, putting them in affect in a privileged position above the law.

On 4 August 1914, World War I began (it still astonishes me that only my generation remembers that date) and Britain found itself without magnetos, watches, binoculars, dyestuffs, fertilizers and food. Naturally everyone felt that something should be done to prevent a recurrence of such a situation and the steps taken after that war were the imposition of massive import duties and the tacit support (by refraining from anti-monopoly legislation) by the government of cartels and monopolies. The vogue word was 'rationalization' meaning horizontal and/or vertical integration of companies and British industry had soon divided up and controlled the home market very comfortably by monopolies or associations of manufacturers, such as ELMA (Electric Lamp manufacturers Association), with private 'star chambers' which punished anyone selling goods below the prices fixed by the association. Of all the grandiose products of rationalisation 'Imperial Chemical Industries' (ICI) was the most grandiose. It was an attempt by Lord Melchett to create the equivalent of the German I G Farbenindustrie; it was to be the 'IG' of the British Empire. So closely did ICI work with the Board of Trade that it began to be regarded as part of the empire by both politicians and the staff of ICI. I remember the response of one senior ICI official when told that we would be importing methanol from USA, 'Well, we would not object to the importation of small quantities, but we could not permit any large import business to develop.'

The policy of rationalisation was unsuccessful because, like other protectionist devices, it restricted not only imports but also exports, and raised the price of goods in the home market.

Since World War II the rate of decline has accelerated and by the mid-1970s Britain was near the bottom of the EEC countries in its productivity per head. For this the politicians must take a large share of responsibility and so much that immoral genius, Maynard Keynes of King's College. The politicians adapted his doctrine of 'spending your way out of a depression' into a highly effective way of buying votes with bread and circuses paid in part by high taxes on industry and in part by printing money.

> In 1949, while the new production plants were going up a decision was made to start production of Araldite in a small way at Duxford as soon as possible. Delivery of most new chemical plant was taking at least two years so the first Araldite plant had to be built almost entirely of second-hand items which R. D. Marsh travelled the country to unearth. In April 1950 the first batches of Araldite epoxy resin went out to customers. . .
>
> Along with the new factory came the need for a new standard of maintenance to deal with the modern ancillary equipment associated with it. The sound maintenance of the chemical plant used for making synthetic resins is an important factor in production. A breakdown may be dangerous; it may also mean the loss of materials costing hundreds of pounds. The day-to-day maintenance of all the chemical plants now occupies about twenty men. The whole Engineering and Maintenance Department employs almost a hundred people. It started life around two men who joined the company in 1940 and 1941, G. Paulger looking after plumbing and engineering, and J. Coxall concerned with buildings and outside installations. Their selfless service and that of others like them has contributed much to our survival and success. In a small and growing organisation it is the maids of all work who are so valuable. Aero Research has been richly blessed with them. Among the first were A. Touhey, G. Paulgar and J. Coxall; R. Potter and L. Barnard were two more, and as time went on there were others.
>
> Towards the end of the 1940s it was clear that chipboard had come to stay. The first of the 'CB' range of 'Aerolite' glues was marketed. Nowadays the 'CB' glues are sold, both here and on the Continent, for the manufacture of a variety of structural materials that go under the generic name of particle board.
>
> The shortage of steel drums in the early 1950s combined with the

desire to reduce process, encouraged us to persuade large users to store glue in bulk and the first delivery of 'Aerolite' glue for bulk storage was made in December 1950 in a hired tanker, while awaiting the first of the company's tanker fleet, which arrived in the following May.

Originally devised by de Trey Freres and developed by CIBA, 'Araldite' epoxy resins have an extraordinary range of characteristics and uses. Their adhesion discovered by Preiswerk and Gams of CIBA is remarkable, their electrical properties and resistance to high temperatures and chemical attack outstanding. These resins have a low shrinkage and contain no volatile solvents.

'Araldite' resins are leading the way to improved designs and new methods of approach in the development of materials for foundry patterns, jigs, fixtures and tooling, reinforced plastics (glasscloth laminates), electrical castings and protective surface coatings.

The year 1951 saw the new production plants settling down and requiring much less labour than the earlier ones. With the centenary Festival of Britain bringing foreign visitors to the country, the opportunity was taken to invite customers from home and abroad to a one-week Summer School held at Duxford and at Cambridge, and 170 came. A somewhat similar school, but called a conference, was arranged in 1957. Here the chief purpose was to bring together people from the aircraft industry, interested in 'Redux' and metal bonding, for an interchange of experiences, each lecturing to and learning from the other. The conference was attended by representatives from eighteen aircraft companies in eight different countries.[43]

In 1953 our Formalin plant was started up. It was based on the BASF plant which I had seen and reported on at Ludwigshafen in 1945 wearing one of Robert Lea's RAF uniforms, using silver as the catalyst to oxidise a mixture of methanol, air and water vapour to formalin and hydrogen. The hydrogen was discharged into the atmosphere from a pipe at the top of the plant. After a thunderstorm it was noticed that evening that there was a plume of flame issuing from this pipe, it was extinguished without untoward effects and a flame detector was installed. R. H. Wilson, who later became managing director, joined us in 1954.

I see that in my speech to the annual works dinner in 1954 I noted that the decline in the population of Duxford had been reversed.

43. C. A. A. Rayner, *Milestones in the History of CIBA (A.R.L.) Limited (1934–59)*, Cambridge1959.

> As long as we have growing pains we cannot suffer from senile decay. How much this firm conceived in a college attic and born in squalor in a corrugated iron shed in Newmarket Road in Cambridge owes to the enthusiasm of its staff. Not haywire enthusiasm but informed enthusiasm. In some professions enthusiasm is not necessarily a virtue. Talleyrand told his young men 'Not too much zeal' (*pas de zele*) and in Winchester Cathedral there is a memorial to a bishop commending his efforts 'to put down enthusiasm.' But nothing great was ever achieved without enthusiasm and (to continue quoting Emerson) though people wish to be settled only as far as they are unsettled is there any hope for them.

On 20 April, 1955, we were honoured by a visit from the Duke of Edinburgh. On my talking to him about his helicopter he most kindly invited my wife and myself to have a ride in it. It was a cheerful and enjoyable occasion on a cloudless spring day.

Ciba (ARL) now had 800 employees and most of my time was taken up with administrative matters. We were doing well, but no new inventions were on the way and we had lost the potentially huge market in USA for aircraft due to lack of interest by the sales organisation there, over which we had no control.

'Co-ordination is the enemy of morale' and increasing pressure was put on me for example to attend meetings, with the managing directors of the other CIBA factories in England, which were time consuming, unproductive and unreal because our respective industries were in such different fields that the possibility of joint effective action was minuscule and we were driven to discuss such matters as the arrangement of intercompany cricket matches. As Sir Lawrence Bragg wisely said the greatest enemy of successful research is a full engagement book. It was time to move on so I announced my resignation on the occasion of the celebration of our twenty five-years of existence.

OUR JUBILEE YEAR

In 1959, the company celebrated its jubilee. We combined the festivities with the opening of a new research block by Dr Robert Kappeli who gave the following address:

Ladies and Gentlemen,

It is an honour for me to address a few words to you today. This is a great occasion and its significance is emphasized by the very impressive preparations and the organization of this ceremony.

In speaking to you today I have to discharge a threefold task.

First of all I am here to deliver on behalf of CIBA Basle a message of congratulation on the twenty-fifth anniversary of the establishment of CIBA (A.R.L.) Limited, or Aero Research, as it was formerly called.

Secondly it is my pleasure to open the new laboratories which have been established here for research in the field of plastics.

Last, but by no means least, I have to say something in reply to the announcement made by Dr de Bruyne that he intends in the near future to withdraw from the active management of this company.

This is quite a large agenda for a short address. Therefore, I must be brief.

It is not possible for me to appraise adequately all that has gone forward at Duxford during the last twenty-five years. I did not meet Dr de Bruyne until after the War, and it was only then that I got to know about his friends and about the factory which they operated here together with him. However, I have since learnt from Dr de Bruyne that the first half of the period upon which we look back today was anything but uneventful. It was a fascinating experiment which this group of men embarked upon; a new venture in the field of chemistry based on a new and original approach to problems of research and production which have engaged the attention and endeavours of Dr de Bruyne and his friends ever since.

Of the second half of the period I have been a close witness. The events of these past twelve years can perhaps be best summarized in the simple words: – what a change in so short a time! From a modest beginning the enterprise has grown into a modern chemical factory which is looked upon as a model of its kind. It is a great achievement of chemistry, engineering, and architectural ability for which everyone concerned deserves warmest congratulations.

However, any industrial plant is just so much tied up capital without the business to support it. Only commercial success can turn the investment involved into an achievement of economic and social significance.

I am happy to say that in the years since the war Duxford has gained a position in the plastics market which is commensurate with the technical progress achieved. This is the result of a sustained effort on the part of those in charge of the commercial side of the venture, and at the same time of close and intelligent co-operation between

CIBA Basle and its adopted child, where both parties have contributed everything in their power towards success.

It would be unseemly for me to boast about Basle's contribution. However, I am free to emphasize the zeal and ability of the research men at Duxford. They have built up the earning power which is the *raison d'etre* of this Company, and have gained for it an enviable reputation for scientific and technical ability and for fair dealing in trade.

We all realise that developments in our industry have assumed the speed of a torrent. To keep afloat and to avoid getting left behind we must always be able to offer newer, more useful, and more valuable products. There is probably no branch of the chemical industry more exposed to the influence of technical progress than the industry of plastics. Survival is dependent on the will and ability to make use of this progress in order to maintain and expand the position achieved, both technically and economically. However, the will alone is not enough. The means to implement it must be made available. That is the reason why it was decided to provide research facilities at Duxford on a generous scale. It is surprising how rapidly and how successfully the decision to do so has been put into effect. Here the reputation of our Company and its leaders has borne fruit. Many considerable problems are involved in assembling a qualified research team and in fitting it into an existing organization. That they have been solved in such a relatively short time is gratifying indeed.

All research needs time to produce results which can be turned to practical account. The difficult path leading from the entry into a certain field to the gathering of experience, to the birth of an idea, and finally to its maturity will have to be trodden at Duxford, as elsewhere. However, there are factors which will operate to our advantage. The research workers can draw upon a valuable fund of past experience and success. Moreover, research at Duxford will not be left entirely to its own resources. The work done here will be supplemented by that of Basle. If all work harmoniously together, our efforts in the field of plastics research will, I am sure, not fail to meet with success. Thanks to the wise guidance which this Company has enjoyed and thanks to CIBA's full understanding of the problems, conditions for smooth co-operation are favourable. This is not only the best guarantee of positive results; it is a stimulating challenge to each and every worker.

In my conception of Duxford's future and the part which it is called upon to play in the CIBA organization, Dr de Bruyne has always been much in the foreground. Twenty-five years ago he started this venture with a small group of friends. He guided it through the difficulties of the early times, and continued to impress his personality on the organization after it had become part of CIBA. There is one of his many qualities, which I should like to emphasize particularly in this connection. It is his unusual talent for guiding a team of co-workers and for creating an atmosphere in which all are happy and full of good will.

This achievement has very little to do with 'enlightened self-interest' – to quote an expression quite often used by Dr de Bruyne himself. His ability as a leader of men stems from a great sense of fairness, from the very nature of a truly cultured gentleman.

This makes Dr de Bruyne's announcement of his intended retirement from the active management a matter which is anything but pleasant for me. I have always hoped that I might be qualified to maintain fruitful relations within our large CIBA group, even with men whose talents and inclinations make them regard the position of individual members within the group in a light which is somewhat different from the usual. A large organization like CIBA, which is dedicated to technical progress, and which, therefore, has the word Science writ large on its programme, raises many problems of this kind, and it has fallen to me to deal with them. From what Dr de Bruyne has mentioned I may infer that his decision is not the result of a failure of my efforts, but that there are other reasons which impel him to take this step. These reasons obviously lie on a higher level. They may be nourished by a desire to penetrate more deeply into the realm of science, that same desire which – applied to the practical requirements of life – has built the industry in which we all have our place. This trend has always been in him. It was fostered by eminent teachers, and now it has evidently triumphed over his other inclinations and talents.

If I reduce this somewhat idealistic interpretation to its practical consequences, I come to another consideration which is worthy of mention. When Dr de Bruyne withdraws from the active management of this Company, he will leave it in a condition which may be something like the vision which he and his friends had twenty-five years ago. What that means can only be fully appreciated by one who has himself taken such a step into the unknown. After a hard struggle Dr de Bruyne found a way to place his venture on firm ground and at the same time to retain its individuality. His achievement has been great, and correspondingly great is our debt of thanks to him. In addition, he solved the problem of his succession. He may now lay down the burden of the office with the happy feeling of having created something lasting and valuable, without ever abandoning anything of the high ethical principles which have always guided his conduct.

We thank Dr de Bruyne for all that he has done for Duxford, and extend to him our best wishes for the realisation of his future plans.

Basle, 6 December 1960.

Dear Dr de Bruyne,

In connection with the farewell dinner given in your honour I have cabled you to-day as follows:

'On the occasion of your retirement as head of CIBA (A.R.L.) Limited I should like to send you my heartiest greetings and to express to you my sincerest thanks, also on behalf of CIBA Limited, Basle, for all the outstanding and devoted service you have rendered in our common cause. personally, it is with greatest satisfaction that I look back over the past years of collaboration with you, and at the same time with admiration for the skill with which you have achieved your high objectives within the framework of such a large concern, always maintaining your own personal convictions and yet promoting the best interests of our organisation.

You are leaving CIBA (A.R.L.) at a time when considerable progress and new and interesting developments are in the offing – at a stage, in fact, from which you as the person responsible may justly derive pride and satisfaction. Your great accomplishments are reflected not only in sales figures and capital assets, but perhaps even more in the enthusiastic and industrious staff which you leave behind you working in a happy and contented atmosphere. Moreover, from the point of view of the CIBA organisation as a whole, you have fostered a spirit of healthy individuality in your company – a success which I should be only too pleased to see repeated in all our branches abroad.

For the future I should like to wish you health and enduring satisfaction in your new field of activity. I look forward very much to meeting you again now and then when the Board of CIBA (A.R.L.) holds its meetings, knowing full well that our personal friendship will in no way have been affected by the decision you have now taken.'

There is a lot more I could add to this cable. Throughout the whole time that we have worked together, we have been faced with a great variety of challenges: sometimes they led to successes from which we both derived pleasure, and sometimes to difficulties of the kind that are always liable to arise in such circumstances and which, thank goodness, we always managed to solve in a spirit of mutual understanding and mutual esteem. I do not wish to go into details here, particularly since the bond between us is fortunately not to be broken now. I know that the friendship which it has been my honour to share with you is based on a similarity of attitude towards important aspects of modern life – an attitude which both of us will possibly still have many opportunities of demonstrating together in practical form.

With renewed heartiest good wishes for your future, I remain

Yours most sincerely,

Robert Kappeli

CHAPTER TEN

EASTERN ELECTRICITY BOARD

ONE morning, to my surprise, I received a letter from Professor Sir Ronald Edwards, chairman of the Electricity Council asking if I would like to be a non-executive director of the Eastern Electricity Board. I accepted and was appointed a director in May 1962 by the Minister of Power, and resigned on 28 February 1967 in view of my immigration to USA

There are some activities which to function satisfactorily have to be monopolies, such as telephones, telegraphs, mail, electricity, and (since the advent of natural gas) gas. This does not mean that they have to be nationalised, but it does imply that there must be some measure of public control over their prices. The Bell Telephone system was an outstanding example of a successful semi-monopoly subject to the regulation of its tariffs by the separate states of USA. On my arrival at Princeton, New Jersey, I asked for a telephone to be installed and within two days a representative called with a variety of instruments ranging from plain ordinary to exotic special. He explained their respective advantages and rates and he there and then installed the instrument of my choice. What a contrast with the GPO system in England where a succession of different administrative officials had to inspect you before (after waiting weeks) a man appeared to actually install the instrument. At that time, in my opinion, 'Ma Bell' ran the best telephone system in the world. Another example of a state regulated semi-monopoly was the 'Public Service Company' in my own state of New Jersey; this had almost a monopoly of the supply of both electricity and natural gas, and generated its electricity. It limited its activities to the supply of these products and did not sell appliances or undertake installation. It had offices but no shops. Advice was impartial and when I complained of the limited capacity of my domestic electric water heater, they recommended the installation of a gas heated one. One meter man of course read both gas and electric meters without having to enter the house. (I am proud to believe that I had some small influence in getting electric meters in the UK installed outside by Eastern Electricity after being told that while this might be possible in USA the meters would not stand up to British climate!)

The Post Office had from the beginning fought for ownership of the telephone system because it saw that it would eventually make its own telegraph system obsolete. Parliament made a compromise which gave the National Telephone Company a franchise for a limited period of time. This was equivalent to a death warrant because the company had to accumulate cash during its life to repay the investors and had no incentive to keep its equipment up to date. Happily the telegraphs in USA were not nationalised and the public was well served by having them run by a public company which for a time at least competed with the Bell Telephone system.

Being on the board of Eastern Electricity was a most interesting experience. The other three non-executive directors were representatives of agricultural, public and trade union interests respectively so although I received no specific instructions it seemed to me that I should try to represent industrial interests.

First and foremost I must pay tribute to the ability of the men and women who ran the concern successfully despite the extra difficulties caused by state ownership. Nearly all of the senior staff had been trained in 'pre-nationalised' electricity concerns. It can be invidious to name individuals, but no one could object to my picking out the former chairman, Mr Derek Wood. I learned much from him and though I differed from him in my opinions on some matters, he was always absolutely free from small mindedness in our discussions. I suppose the biggest development during my term of office was the installation of the Honeywell Computer at Ipswich. In 1968-9 there were 63 employees for 10,000 customers, in 1977-8 only 38 employees for 10,000 customers.

The extra difficulties caused by state ownership were:

1 The absence of shareholders meant that profitability was not a prime concern of management which was under con stant pressure from 'pressure groups' particularly farmers. After the nationalisation of the coal mines notices were displayed informing members of the public that they now ' owned the coal mines', but the interests of the general public

in a state concern cannot be compared with that of men and women who have invested their savings in it.

2. The inability to raise money on the open market meant that the Treasury was in financial control; consistently acted as a brake.
3. The nationalisation of the electricity supply and the effect of the 'closed shop' has made it an easy target for trade unions who can, of course, also bring political pressure to bear. A favourite trick is to obtain wage increase for the lowest paid members on humanitarian grounds and then later on to demand 'restoration of differentials' in fairness to skilled workers.
4. Ever-changing directives issued by ever-changing ministers make onsistent policies difficult. One minister forbad adver tising – no doubt in accordance with good Fabian doctrine. An equally absurd directive was issued to the GPO Telephone System ordering a return of money to its customers even though the creaking Strowger exchanges are in desperate need of replacement.

A good feature of the British electricity supply organisation in the mid-1970s was the separation between the generation and the sales of electricity. The Central Electricity Generating Board (CEGB) generated electricity for the whole country and distributed it by its own extra high voltage 'grid' to its customers who were the area boards. The area boards were responsible for local distribution and sales. The CEGB was able to build generating stations of an economical size and to distribute the power through the grid in accordance with hour by hour changes in demand. Due to Victorian legislation electricity up to World War I was generated locally by small stations which could not be interconnected. The use of electricity for heating was more widespread than in USA due to the use of storage heaters.

The least successful and, from an ethical point of view, least desirable activity of the area boards was their shopkeeping business. The operating profit made by Eastern Electricity in 1977-8 on contracting and sales of appliances was £2,938,000 (according to the published accounts) which was not a good figure in relation to the capital employed. But like 'British Gas' (their competitor in the sale of energy), whose accounts were described in the *Financial Times* of

25 July 1979 as: 'A mass of confusing figures none being more misleading than the declared pretax figure of £360.7M (profit) against £180.3M (in previous year)', the annual report of Eastern Electricity did not reveal all. It did not, for example, divulge the real capital employed.

Nor did the accounts reveal that less than half of the 'shopkeeping' profit was derived from contracting and sales and that the greater portion arose from interest on hire purchase. This was a purely financial operation in which Eastern Electricity borrowed money at the going rate from the taxpayer via the Electricity Council and the Treasury and lent it back to those of its (taxpaying) customers foolish enough to pay interest on it at the rate of 25 per cent a year.

Figures in Appendix 2 of the accounts were misleading because they were merely historic figures and I am informed that in mid-1970s money values the shopkeeping turnover became £44.6M for 1968-9 compared with £45.4M in 1978-9. In other words it was a 'no growth' business.

Many of the shops were freehold and in excellent positions. A good deal of capital could have been released by their sale. The Eastern Electricity Board defended its retention of shops not because they were shops but because they were places where customers could pay accounts and make personal contact with the organisation. But a counter in a shopping centre or a bus station was all that was needed.

The Board complained that it was not allowed to diversify as much as it would like in its range of goods for sale. It appeared to forget its disastrous entry into the radiogramophone business.

It was a most interesting part-time job and I was sorry to have to leave it.

18. The initial set up for making honeycombs, April 1954

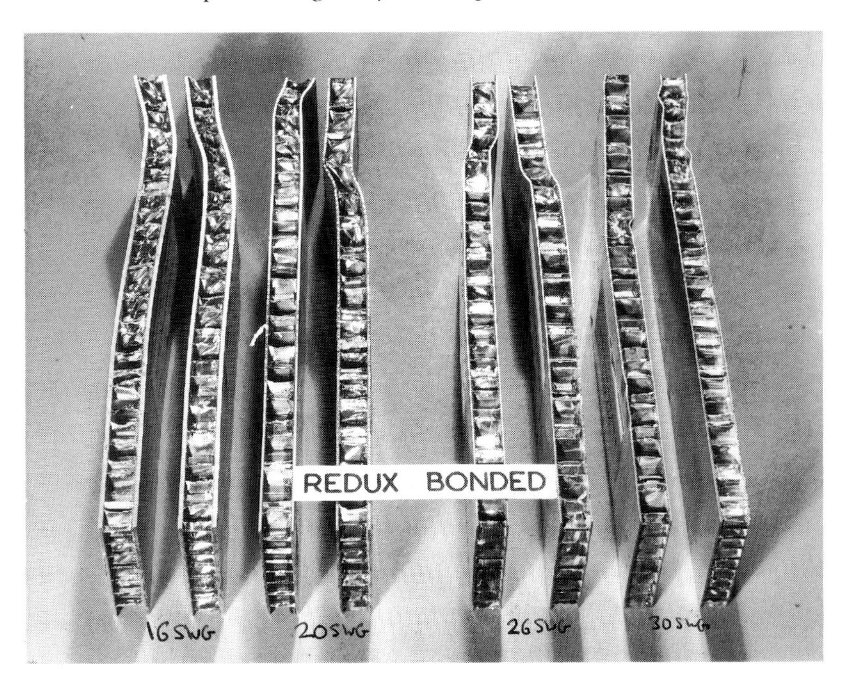

19. Redux bonded sandwich construction – tested to destruction.

20. Techne (Cambridge) Ltd, Duxford, incorporated in 1948 to make and sell scientific instruments.

21. Techne Inc, Princeton, New Jersey. In 1961, permission was granted to set up a branch of Techne (Cambridge) Ltd in the USA.

22. Plaque commemorating the opening of the de Bruyne Building at CIBA-Geigy, Duxford, 7 September 1987.

23. The Boeing 777 – an example of how the pioneering work of Aero Research Ltd is still relevant in the 1990s.

24. On the occasion of my ninetieth birthday at Trinity College, Cambridge, 8 November 1994. *Left to right*: (standing): Sir Andrew Huxley and Sir Michael Atiyah; (sitting) Sir Arthur Marshall and myself.

CHAPTER ELEVEN

'A HAPPIER SEAT'

Warned by Celestial Omens, we retreat to seek in
foreign Lands a Happier Seat *Dryden*

IN January 1967 I sent out about fifty copies of a letter of which its substance is reproduced below:

Ever since a Royal Commission on Awards to Inventors made me an award I have been unable to deny that I am an inventor, though the description is almost as pejorative as that of director, which I am too.

Inventors and directors in their selfish ways (often unwittingly) contribute to the wealth of a nation and I believe that the most useful kind of inventor is the inventor-owner-director who commands both knowledge and resources. But such an individual is now thought to be undesirable (if not already obsolete) by those economists and others who, in the Finance Act 1965 for instance, seek to ensure that he will be snuffed out. They believe that modern technological advances require such enormous resources that only large firms or the Government can make successful inventions; but in my opinion the proper conclusion to be drawn is that as always an individual must choose his research programme carefully. The evidence is that most of the significant and really original inventions have come from individuals. My predicament was foreseen in the prophetic words of Edison:

'Socialism, if it ever arrives, must provide unlimited incentive for its executive minds and its creators. Unlimited incentive. The motive that I have for inventing is, I guess, like the motive of the billiard player, who always wants to do a little better – to add to his record. Under present circumstances I use the reasonable profit which I derive from one invention to make experiments looking toward another invention. If socialism gave me the means to continue inventing, I would invent; but if it failed to do so, or began to tie me down, I would quit!'

I have thought a good deal during the past twelve months about what will be best for Techne (with its 100 or so men and women who constitute its real capital) and best for permitting me to continue my life as I have always run it. The conclusion I have reached is that I can achieve these objectives, though not without penalties, by moving my own base to USA where five years ago I established a branch of Techne at Princeton, NJ and which shows promise of becoming a vigorous viable concern. In this way I hope to keep myself free to help Techne and incidentally this little island in which I have been brought up.

Below are some of the more interesting replies.

From Lord Adrian, Trinity College, Cambridge (2 February 1967):

My dear de Bruyne,

When I first read your letter, it filled me with gloom, but on rereading it I see that at least you will have connections here which will, I hope, make you come back from time to time (I hope it will be in the Concorde rather than the corresponding Boeing). I thought that there were very few inventors unattached to big companies even in the U.S.A. nowadays, but I can well believe that they are given much more latitude – I remember Langmuir for instance. But you have always been the almost unique example of the inventor who has never surrendered his true independence even to Rutherford. I can well appreciate that you may not want to be run by the present Minister of Technology. Anyway the older generation here will look forward to seeing you again from time to time (each time looking, I hope, more prosperous than the last). I am inclined to think that Trinity will never be as full of men with ideas as it was when you were here between the wars, but at all events a visit from you will remind us of a great time.

Best wishes to you both – and au revoir.

Adrian

From Sir Barnes Wallis, White Hill House, Effingham, Surrey (2 February, 1967):

Dear de Bruyne,

Very many thanks for your most interesting letter of the 1st February.

I entirely agree with your experience that progress is made by individuals and not by these tremendous mergers. I think that the present deplorable state of the Aircraft Industry in this country is very largely due to the amalgamation which was forced on them by Mr Duncan Sandys.

It is most interesting to learn that you and your wife are leaving for the USA While the fact that you propose to leave this country fills me with dismay and sorrow, in another way I am very pleased because I believe that I shall shortly be joining you, and to have a friend in that vast country will be a very great advantage.

With kindest regards, and very best wishes,

Yours sincerely,

Barnes Wallis

From the Vice-Chancellor, the University of Newcastle Upon Tyne (6 February 1967):

The University of Newcastle Upon Tyne
The Vice-Chancellor
C.I.C. Bosanquet, M.A., D.C.L.

Dear de Bruyne,

It was most friendly of you to send me a copy of your letter dated February 1st, giving the bad news of your move to Princeton and the reasons for it.

I wish I could talk to you about all this. Is there a chance that I could persuade you and your wife to pay us a short visit before March 31st, to meet a group of industrialists and dons here and to talk about the supremely important issues which you raise? I fear that you may be too busy in your last two months; but if, either now or on one of your return visits before I retire in the summer of 1968, you would care to come here please let me know.

Please let me have your address in Princeton. We have two married daughters and six grandchildren on that side of the Atlantic, and many friends in Princeton, so we may ring your door-bell in the future.

Yours sincerely

Charles Bosanquet

My reply:

Dear Charles,

How characteristic of you to reply with a personal letter to my printed one and to include an invitation to come and talk to a live body of men! I cannot accept I am afraid because, as you suggest, I am running short of time (rather a poor excuse – aren't we all short of time?) and also because I believe England is set on an irreversible course (a shocking excuse implying that nothing can be done – a counsel of despair and perhaps even a bit of bloody mindedness).

It may be that England is just having a protracted menopause and I shall come back to find Enoch Powell as P.M. But I doubt it.

I enclose my address in Princeton and if one day your wife and you press on our illuminated automatic chiming door bell (I did not install it!) that would be the happiest day I can imagine.

Yours ever,

Norman

From Professor Sir Ronald Edwards, The Electricity Council, 30 Millbank, London, SW1 (7 February 1967):

Dear Norman,

Anthony Wedgwood Benn, the Minister of Technology, was lunching with me the other day and when I got back to the office your circular letter was there. I took the liberty of showing your letter to him and sending him a copy of the paper you gave in my seminar, saying that I thought it might be worthwhile his hearing at first hand what a person such as yourself felt about the brain drain and all that, and why you should think the American climate the better one for the development of your interests.

He dropped me a line this morning saying he would be very glad to have a talk with you, and if you agree to this – which I very much hope you will – could you get in touch with his office to fix a mutually convenient time? If you don't know Wedgwood Benn I can ssure you you will like him and find him very intelligent.

I hope you will not be cross with me and tell me that I should have minded my own business. It is my business, all our business when people like you start leaving the country, even if only half-time!

Yours Ronnie

From the late J.A. McNeilly, Arthur H. Thomas Company, Philadelphia, PA, USA (27 February 1967):

Dr Norman A de Bruyne
Techne (Cambridge) Ltd
Duxford, Cambridge
England

Dear Dr de Bruyne:

Thank you for sending me a copy of your Duxford Manifesto. In that it announces your decision to come to live in America, I am glad. In that it means for you a severance from your beloved Cambridge, I feel it a rotten shame.

As for your little insertion that it is all my doing, I wonder whether you are blaming me for the rise of British Socialism. I'll confess to having read Robin Hood many years ago, but not aspiring to politics, I put it down as delightful juvenile fiction and went on to Balzac.

You can be certain that we sincerely hope that you and Mrs de Bruyne will be happy in Princeton. If there is anything we can do to help ensure this, please let me know.

Sincerely,

Joe

From the late Leonard Weiss, ScD, Roswell Park Memorial Institute, Buffalo, New York (3 March 1967):

Dear de Bruyne,

I was vastly amused at your Directorial Statement. You might let me have the brunette's telephone number!

At a far humbler level, my own experiences have been pretty much the same as your own. I would think that you cannot fail to find things much better over here. Life in the US certainly has its drawbacks, but the most important thing which I enjoy here is the ability of the individual to carry the responsibility for his own research – profit and loss.

I hope that we might meet again before too long.

With kindest regards.

Yours sincerely

Leonard Weiss

Lord Cross, Royal Courts of Justice, London (6 February 1967):

Dear Norman

This is the first time that I have had personal experience with 'brain drain'! – I am so sorry; – but I am sure that you are right – and good luck!

From the Minister Richard Marsh, Thames House South, Millbank, London (13 February 1967):

Dear De Bruyne,

I am indeed sorry to learn from your letter of 28th January, that the country and, more particularly, the Eastern Electricity Board are to lose your valuable advice and experience.

In accepting your resignation from part-time membership of the Eastern Electricity Board with effect from the last day of this month, I should like to thank you most warmly for all you have done for the Board during the past five years.

I wish you every success in your new sphere which I shall look forward to hearing more about from you personally when I come to lunch with the Board on Friday 24th February.

Yours sincerely,

Richard Marsh

CALLAGHAN'S FINANCE ACT 1965

In the letter of January 1967 which I sent to my friends I mentioned the Finance Act of 1965 as one of the reasons for my decision to emigrate to USA. This Act introduced a capital-gains tax on current transactions and on the death of the owner of a privately-owned limited company (called a 'close company'); since then the position has been further complicated by a gifts tax. Until this Act there was still some hope and incentive for the owner to build up his business in the knowledge that he could dispose of it at a (hopefully substantial) profit to provide for a new venture, or for his retirement, or for his family (subject to death duties); it is of course extremely onerous in an inflationary situation which produces 'paper' capital profits. Apart from this, the Act became especially burdensome on privately-owned limited companies 'close companies'.

The Act called for a distribution of 60 per cent of profits 'less so much as the company shows cannot be distributed without prejudice to the company's business' – the Inland Revenue being of course the final arbiter. Loan interest paid to an individual shareholder was not deductible for corporation tax. The owner paid surtax at the top rate on the company's distributions. If, for example, the close company made an extra hundred pounds profit before taxation, then the Inland Revenue takes up to £72.85 (£40 corporation tax and £32.85 income tax and surtax) leaving the owner with £3.15 and the company with £24, which carries a contingent liability to £7.2 capital-gains tax.

In the original Act the remuneration of directors was limited to £4,000 a year. Some of the more vindictive provisions have since been modified for example the charges on death was repealed in 1971 presumably because it was realised that vindictiveness can lose votes but the act remains as a record of Mr Callaghan's outlook which he himself boasted to be 'to squeeze the lemon until the pips squeak'.

THE MINISTER AND MINISTRY OF TECHNOLOGY ('MINTECH')

Following the correspondence with Sir Ronald Edwards, I took the lift to the eleventh floor of the Ministry of Technology on or about 14 March 1967 to call on the Minister, who directed 23,000 scientists, technologists, research workers and others in eighteen state research and development establishments. In an interview I had just read, reported by John Gale (the *Observer,* 19 February 1967), he said:

> I was born on this site. Did you know that? The house I was born in was torn down to make room for this building. And the Webbs lived here, so this building has the ghosts of Sidney and Beatrice Webb . . . The job here is to help create in this country an industrial organization strong enough to compete . . . The giant American corporations are so strong that they can spend a lot on research, development, marketing and management skills. Bigger means better? I think so, actually. Everything's getting bigger; schools are getting bigger, local government's getting bigger, machines are getting bigger. Super-powers are the big powers. Within this, the scope for the individual is much bigger than before . . . I'm interested in technology spiritually, because it liberates the mind . . . I'm not so worried about the Brain-Drain as some people, because this country will be an increasingly exciting place to work in. The electromagnet is switched on.

Somewhere between 1945 and 1969, killing and calculating powers become greater than communication and travelling powers. Then they all hit the sky. Mr Benn studied political science at Oxford; if he had gone to Princeton he might have attended a course on physics for non-scientists and would have learned that the important things in such charts are not the curves but the plotted points which are the only known facts. Where are the points through which Mr Benn drew his curves? This chart is not even a 'rough indication,' – it is a travesty.

As the lift accelerated my head seemed to move down towards my feet in sympathy with my despondent mood. Why had I come? What good would it do?

As far as I can remember, he asked me why I was emigrating and I replied that the last straw had been Mr Callaghan's Finance Act of 1965 which had removed all incentive and hope for the lone 'enterpriser.' His comment was the one that I had heard before from a member of Parliament (a Tory member) – 'I am not a taxation expert' – made in the tone of voice appropriate to expressing ignorance of a recondite subject such as ophiology; but coming from a member of the cabinet I found it shocking.

It seemed to me to be a waste of time to discuss the material I had prepared with a man who, while unconcerned with the details of Callaghan's budget, nevertheless must have approved of it as a member of the cabinet; perhaps as a Fabian he would approve of any measure to reduce incentives to a profit-making (and competitive) businessman without worrying about the details?

Benn went on to say, 'You are emigrating for a negative reason, not for a positive one' perhaps unconsciously plagiarising D. H. Lawrence writing about the pilgrim fathers: 'What did they come for? For lots of reasons. Perhaps least of all in search of freedom of any sort; positive freedom that is. They came largely to get away – the most simple of motives. To get away.'

But I was leaving because men like Benn had created a social system, contrary to the tenets on which I had built my life. What could one usefully say to a man who went straight from school to the RAF to Oxford, to the BBC and (at the age of 25) to the House of Commons? Who, unlike his uncle Sir Ernest Benn had no experience of business life, or of the disciplines of real science or technology and who as chairman of the Fabian Society presumably believed in 'the Fabian socialist philosophy with its emphasis on "social justice" and its denigration of those principles of competition and of reward for effort which are needed for dynamic growth in an economy?'

He then hinted at great things being hatched out of his department for the future of the country; but as I thought that my greatest way of helping the country would be to increase Techne's exports from Cambridge to Princeton, I did not ask to be allowed to join in the fun. After some chitchat I left 'by that same door as in I went' and was glad to get out into the comparatively fresh air of London's traffic.

What was Benn doing at the time with his department? The story begins with my friend Patrick Blackett, who had won the confidence of Wilson, prime minister of the Labour Government that came into office in 1964, promising to link 'socialism to science and science to socialism' in 'the white heat of a scientific revolution'. It would improve the international status of British industry by directing it along sound scientific principles and with new technological advances. The great success of Blackett and other scientists in World War II would be repeated in peace time. But the trouble was that in practice Mintech officials simply didn't know what to do to achieve the goals set for their department. By 1967 Mintech and the white hot revolution were recognised to be nonstarters, though Blackett was still rather despairingly preaching his gospel, which demanded belief in at least two dogmas:

(1) that successful technology innovation can be envisaged as consisting of a sequence of related steps: pure science, applied science, invention, development, prototype construc tion production, marketing, sales and profit;
(2) that British industry was fragmented and 'defragmentation' should be spurred on by pressure from the government.

Recently I found a note which I had written on the bottom of a letter from Lord Adrian: 'Adrian in conversation on Saturday 18 Feb. 1967 referring to the current fashion for forcing firms to amalgamate said, "It's all because Blackett found larger convoys were better than small ones in the war; we had it all expounded at the Parliamentary Sciences Committee." He was presumably referring to the meeting on 16 February when perhaps for the first time Blackett was openly critical of the government.'

In 1966 Benn had become minister of Mintech but instead of closing down the expensive and ineffective empire which he had inherited and, in Gladstone's words, letting the money fructify in the pockets of the people, he decided to disguise it in the clothes of a fairy godmother. Mintech would prescribe financial support to business by purchase of equity, 'industrial democracy', nationalisation, compulsory amalgamation etc. Mintech's infinite wisdom would prescribe just the right medicine for the patient's illness and of course Benn would do all he could to ward off competition from the common market. Presumably these were 'the great things' to which he was referring in his conversation with me.

A government department can do nothing to encourage industrial research that cannot be better done by the Chancellor of the Exchequer. The Finance Act of 1944 did more for industrial research than anything the Department of Scientific & Industrial Research (DSIR) did. I believe that research undertaken by government authorities is simply the lesser of two evils, the alternative being no research at all, and that with some exceptions cooperative research associations have been failures. I am in entire agreement with Dr F. Oederlin of the Sulzer organisation which he wrote:

> In the prosecution of research work the engineering industry should depend on its own initiative and wherever possible on its own financial

> resources, and not upon direct state aid, which can be replaced by other forms of encouragement, such as the reduction of taxation on research undertakings. Purposeful and scientifically pursued industrial research is bound to the works which promotes it and cannot be separated from the manufacturing departments. It has always been courageous private initiative which, in the free play of competitive forces, has produced the economically valuable triumphs of engineering.[44]

But Mr Benn told me that I was out of date and no doubt today he would say I am now even more out of date because, even in the USA, a government agency (NASA) had to be set up to direct a space programme too expensive to be carried out by industry alone. But this is not industrial research to produce products to be sold on the market and moreover 'the fundamental discoveries in regard to high altitude rocket propulsion, as distinct from the refinement and development of these ideas, were made by independent enthusiasts working with limited resources under discouraging conditions and for long ridiculed or ignored by the main bodies of organized Science and Technology.'

The difference in the treatment of enterprise between the United Kingdom and the United States is exemplified in Professor Dennis Gabor's lecture on the Hologram (his own invention) to the Royal Institute 7 February 1969.[45]

> In holography we have an example of the not unusual case that an invention is made in this country, and becomes a practical success in the United States of America. This, I feel, requires if not an apology at least an explanation. The diagnosis is simple; the remedy, I am afraid, is not so easy. If one follows the success story in the United States of such modern inventions as the laser, or holography, it is evident that it was due not so much to the industrial giants, as to new, comparatively small enterprises. It is true, the ruby-laser was invented by T. H. Maiman at Hughes, the helium-neon laser by Ali Javan in the Bell Telephone Laboratories; both very large firms. But the giants had not even started to move when a number of small firms, several of them newly founded, had flooded the market with lasers. This is even more true of holography. The three firms which have so far made an industrial success of it, Conductron, GC Optronics and KMS, are small and new science-based enterprises, all three grouped around the campus of the University of Michigan, Ann Arbor, like the famous 'Route 128' factories grouped

44. F. Oederlin, *Aero Research Technical Notes,* 1945–6.
45. Published in the *Proceedings of the Royal Institution,* Vol. 43 (1970), pp. 35–70.

> around the MIT. It was such comparatively small and new firms – .which have grown rapidly to respectable dimensions, with many million dollars of turnover per year – always founded by highly energetic young presidents, who are always owners or part-owners, and in many cases the inventors of the devices which they manufacture, who have made the laser and holography a success before the industrial giants even started to move. And it is just this type of scientific entrepreneur, without a thought of bankruptcy but fully confident, and in most cases rightly confident of success which is hardly existent in this country. Their race was fairly widespread in the nineteenth century, but is now almost extinct. So I am afraid that it is no use yearning platonically for American efficiency. We cannot have it if we disown the American system of values!

In England a generation has grown up that has never experienced (and has been taught to despise) the freedom of capitalism and has only known a situation where comparative poverty is the norm. As Winston Church said, 'Capitalism is the unequal distribution of prosperity and socialism is the equal distribution of poverty.' Howard W. Johnson, president of Massachusetts Institute of Technology, pointed out that 50 per cent of the entrepreneurs who start a small technologically advanced company have come from homes in which the father was self-employed, and is typically in his early thirties.[46] Since the objectives of the British socialism is to maximize the number of employees working for the state it would seem that the main source of originality and risk taking in the next generation in Britain will disappear.

My wife and I left Southampton for New York on 31 March 1967 on the *United States.*

46. *Science*, Vol. 160 (10 May 1968), pp. 620–7.

CHAPTER TWELVE

USA

TECHNE (Cambridge) Ltd was incorporated in August 1948 to make and sell scientific instruments. Its office and workshop were in the attic of Duxford Mill which Robert Lea had bought and renovated as his home. It soon outgrew this situation and took over Duxford rectory which the rector gladly gave up to move into a smaller and more easily maintained house in the village. Before the war I had had tea in the rectory drawing room and it was a pleasure to look out across the garden and the glebe up the valley of the Cam towards Ickleton. Then Aero Research Ltd came and partly obscured the view, followed by a council house estate which obliterated it. The quiet lane which led from the village to the rectory and ambled on to cross the River Cam at the ford near Hinxton was now a suburban road. My sympathies warmed to those maligned pioneers of the industrial revolution who produced the 'Black Country', like Mr Hornblower I had spoiled the view, but if one is to provide employment for a thousand people there is little choice.

The nominal Capital of Techne Ltd was £1,000 and Robert Lea and I were the shareholders. We thought it would be an interesting weekend hobby, and it did not become a serious occupation for me until I left CIBA (ARL) Ltd at the beginning of 1961. In August of that year we opened a sales office in Princeton, New Jersey, USA following the success in USA of its 'Tempunit' temperature controller for water baths. This had a pneumatic amplifier powered by the suction produced by the stirrer in the water resulting in an inherent 'fail safe' system which ensured that the heater was turned off if the water level fell; it also eliminated the bulky valves or 'tubes' necessary in an electronic temperature control system before the days of the transistor. When I showed it to Mr Paterson in about 1957, president of the A. H. Thomas Company in

Philadelphis, he commented, 'Someone at Techne has been having disturbed nights dreaming up this device!' I came away with a firm order.

In 1961 we were given permission to set up a branch of Techne (Cambridge) Ltd in USA and we found a disused community centre on route US1, close to the intersection with the road to the University of Princeton, and near enough to be in the Princeton postal area. It was too large for our immediate needs although in other respects ideal. But there was a snag. It was just inside a residential area called Penn's Neck (a neck is an eighteenth-century word for a 'parcel of land') and we would have to get a 'zoning variance' from West Windsor Township to permit its use for light industry. A township is I believe an area whose perimeter permitted a rider on horseback to get round it in a day. Our lawyer thought our variance would be difficult, our realtor of course thought it could be done. We collected what signatures we could and on a hot moonlit August night presented our petition at the little court house at Dutch Neck, with background music provided by a chorus of crickets. Almost everyone of the speakers was against us but in the end the mayor and his committee gave us our variance. It was grass roots democracy at work and somehow attractively old fashioned like a Swiss cantonal meeting. I had a similar feeling of being carried back to a simpler time when I called on the First National Bank of Princeton and went direct to Mr Poe, chairman of the bank seated at a long table at the back of the premises but not screened or in any way inaccessible. He did not need to refer to 'head office' he was the head office.

The building and the car park cost $60,000 and he said that it was a good bargain. He agreed to give us a mortgage at 5½ per cent interest, fixed by state law for the term of the mortgage. He made one stipulation – that we should buy our heating oil from the Nassau Oil Co!

Now the private bank has almost disappeared and its place has been taken by impersonal organisations with public relations experts speaking with forked tongues.

We decided to build a house in a corner of the parking lot and chose one called 'The Golden Zenith' out of a catalogue. Then the full power of American efficiency became apparent. The whole operation was directed from an office on US1. The work on the site was done by subcontractors who followed one another in a tight sequence beginning with the excavator who bulldozed out the basement in a day and ending with the painters six weeks later. It was of course a wooden house complying with regulations about insulation, drainage etc. and it is the house in which my wife and I went to live in 1967. It was excellently planned and we took in the garage and porch space provided in the original design to make a large living room. The only part of the structure that wore out was the floor in one of the bathrooms made of small tiles stuck (is my face red?) to a urea formaldehyde-wood particle 'chip board' which proved unable to withstand the splashes of water from the shower.

I am often asked why I chose Princeton. My first glimpse of Princeton was in 1953 when returning on US1 from Pennsylvania to New York City. My companion made a detour to show the town to me and it looked like an oasis in the squalor of much of New Jersey. Nevertheless I first fancied the neighbourhood of Boston as I liked New England, and Boston is closer to London Airport than is New York. However my friends at Arthur H. Thomas said, 'You don't want to tuck yourself away in a corner up there' so I decided on Princeton which reminded me of Cambridge, England and had all the facilities of libraries etc.' of a leading University. It is about half way between New York and Philadelphia and has excellent communications. I have no doubts that it was a good choice.

When my wife and I took up residence in 'Golden Zenith' in April 1967 we made it a rule to refrain from making generalisations about USA for at least six months. Now after twenty years of residence and almost thirty years of citizenship I can only generalise that USA is a successful league of nations populated by the most self-critical and litigious people in the world. The financial freedoms regained were invigorating. I could travel abroad instantly without permission and take as much money as I liked. There were still incentives to earn income; higher incomes did not attract penal taxation. I could bequeath my estate (modest by US standards) including my business and pay only marginal death duties. I could invest in US and foreign securities without paying a premium. I could deduct charitable bequests from my income before tax.

I set up a new US company called Techne Inc with a capital of $10,000 wholly owned by me and I paid Techne Ltd $70,000 for its US business.

Another feature of our former community centre was that we had a railroad station just outside our side door, on the single track electric railway popularly known as the 'Dinky Line' between Princeton Junction and Princeton. 'Station' is admittedly too grand a name but it had a shelter and seat for intending passengers. By waving at the oncoming train as it came into view round a curve, one could get it to stop and if it overshot it would politely reverse. Alas it was too good to last and one day a team of hard hats removed all traces of it. The Pennsylvania Railroad had long made clear that it wanted to get rid of the 'Dinky Line' and at one time made a cunning but unsuccessful beginning by calling Princeton Junction 'Princeton'.

I became a citizen of USA on 10 November 1972. In 1979, aged 75, I was still able to do development work in my laboratory and I produced a stirrer for cell suspension culture and microcarrier culture operated by threephase air which overcame the disadvantages of the conventional magnetic stirrer. I also produced an orbital shaker of K pneumatic design which was inexpensive.

Patrick H. Summers was the first president of Techne Inc employing eighteen persons and J. M. Pearson was the first managing director of Techne (Cambridge) Ltd employing one hundred. Techne Inc was, except for my own activities, a selling organisation.

EPILOGUE

NORMAN DE BRUYNE'S NINETIETH BIRTHDAY

I am delighted to be here, representing Trinity College, for Norman de Bruyne's 90th birthday. It's a happy occasion and I am sure there will be many of you here who will have known Norman for many years, and who could tell from first hand knowledge something of his remarkable career. I myself went up to Trinity as an undergraduate in 1949, five years after Norman left. But we have many Senior Fellows who go back a long way and so I have been able to call on the collective memory of the College. We even have one Fellow who celebrated his 90th birthday last year and remembers de Bruyne as a young student. That is Sir Charles Oatley who has asked me to convey his warmest greetings to his fellow nonagenarian. By a coincidence another Trinity man, now living in Edinburgh, is also today celebrating his 90th birthday. Professor William Edge, who lectured to my wife at Edinburgh University, was elected to his Research Fellowship at Trinity on the same day in October 1928 as Dr de Bruyne.

From being a Research Fellow Norman moved on to being our Junior Bursar for six years. This is a key post in College and involves looking after all the College buildings and, even more tricky, how to slot the undergraduates into them. It is a task that requires many qualities and it is an excellent training ground for life beyond the College, as Norman de Bruyne's career shows.

This century could be characterized in many ways, but it would not be unreasonable to describe it as the century of the aeroplane. Those whose lives have spanned most of the century will therefore have seen, or taken part in, the development of aviation from its early beginnings. Norman belongs to that generation and aeroplanes, in one way or another, have been a main theme in his life. Here in the Cambridge area he was much involved from the very earliest days with what started out as Marshall's Flying School (he was their first pupil) and is now a substantial centre for aircraft engineering. The history of Marshall's has just recently appeared and Norman, together with a number of Trinity colleagues, such as F. A. Simpson, G. I. Taylor and John Burnaby, figures very prominently in the book.

Sir Arthur Marshall, who wrote the book, described himself as a life-long friend and I am glad to say he celebrated his 90th birthday last December. Sir Arthur describes the unusual events surrounding his own wedding at which Norman was best man. The married couple left on their honeymoon, not by limousine, but by Puss Moth monoplane and when they returned to Cambridge the Junior Bursar of Trinity converted some undergraduate lodgings for their use. I am glad the College was able to help, though I am not sure that Junior Bursars nowadays have quite the same leeway!

After learning to fly and qualifying as a ground engineer and aircraft welder at de Havilland's, Norman went on, over a four-year period, to design and build his own very original monoplane 'The Snark', which he flew all over Europe, and which was subsequently bought for research purposes by the Air Ministry.

Another noteworthy and perhaps rash joint undertaking by Arthur Marshall and Norman de Bruyne was on 4 August 1939. On the spur of the moment they decided to fly to Danzig to see what all the fuss was about. The return journey via Warsaw but avoiding Berlin is a bit tense and something of a close call.

Norman's interest in aircraft led in 1934 to his acquiring a site in Duxford and establishing Aero Research Limited 'to bridge the gap between research and development, manufacture and practical use of new structural materials for aircraft'.

Building wooden aircraft aroused his interest in synthetic resins as providing superior glues and led in due course to 'Aerolite', 'Araldite' and other successful products. The de Havilland Mosquito was one of the famous aircraft that was held together by Aero Research adhesives.

The company was so successful that it needed major expansion and this led to its merger with CIBA/GEIGY and its transformation into a major, probably the largest manufacturer of its type in Europe.

Having launched one major company successfully, Norman later founded a separate firm (Techne) for the development and manufacture of scientific instruments, this time based in Princeton, New Jersey. I have only just realised that, just as Norman was establishing his new enterprise in Princeton, I was also settling in at the Institute for Advanced Study there. So, for many years, we must have been close neighbours. I am glad that, now that Norman is back in this country and I have returned to Trinity as Master, we are close neighbours once again.

Speaking in my other capacity as President of the Royal Society, I am particularly pleased that Norman's scientific contributions were recognized in 1967 by his election as an FRS. The citation at the time read:

> Distinguished for his practical application of science to certain problems in aircraft construction, especially the use of plastic materials and adhesives . . . by making a glued metal-to-metal joint a practicable proposition de Bruyne made possible new and lighter forms of aircraft structure which are more resistant to fatigue and crack propagation...

The certificate was signed by P. M. S. Blackett, J. D. Cockroft, G. I. Taylor and T. E. Allibone (over 90 and still going strong).

Perhaps I can close by quoting from a letter Norman wrote to Arthur Marshall shortly after they had both turned 80. Passing on the advice from a friend, he says:

> I have good news for you. The first eighty years are the hardest. The second eighty, so far as my experience goes, is a succession of birthday parties. Everybody wants to carry your baggage and help you up the stairs.
>
> At eighty you can relax with no misgivings. You have a perfect alibi for everything. At seventy people are mad with you. At eighty they forgive everything. If you ask me life begins at eighty.

I hope Norman has enjoyed his life since 80 and that he continues to enjoy the next decade as well. Perhaps I can ask all of you to join me in drinking his health.

Sir Michael Atiyah, 8 November 1994

NORMAN DE BRUYNE – 90

Dr Norman de Bruyne or DB as he is widely known, will be 90 on November 8th, which may explain why he is not cycling around the village and factory or driving his Sinclair electric chair. But what a 90 years! While a physicist at Cambridge University he founded the Cambridge Aircraft Company at Marshalls Airfield, to build light aircraft. He designed a 4-seater low-wing monoplane (he 'Snark') and built it over three years – during which time he qualified as a licensed welder and ground engineer.

Studying 'For Sale' columns in the paper for a bandsaw he saw land for sale at Duxford. As he wanted an airfield, he cycled out and bought it. So his company became Aero Research Ltd at Duxford in April 1934.

The Snark was nearing completion. It had folding wings, carried four people and luggage and cruised at 110mph. Initially rejected by Airworthiness authorities, a Snark fuselage was tested to destruction. Impressive results led to the Airworthiness Certificate and the Snark was flown by DB in December 1934.

About this time he became a consultant to De Havilland Aircraft Co. with particular reference to plastics in aircraft. An early project of A.R.L. was to find new glues for aircraft. Casein glues were used in Snark construction and the plywood was held together by blood. A consultant to A.R.L. at the University produced an experimental urea-formaldehyde glue. Encouraging tests led to a pilot plant for the glue known as 'Aerolite'. Air Ministry approval for aircraft use was given in 1937. 'Aerolite' glues, produced in thousands of tonnes at Duxford, are now widely used in many countries and in most world based industries (including plywood, chipboard and furniture manufacture).

In 1937 DB read a paper, 'Plastic Materials in Aircraft Construction' for which he received the Simms Gold Medal. He showed that fibre reinforced phenolic resins could be light and strong enough for aircraft construction. A friend in the linen business suggested flax as the reinforcement, and when combined with phenolic this was known as Gordon Aerolite.

In the war, with aluminium in short supply, an experimental Spitfire fuselage was built of it and fully met the specification. The need for plastic Spitfires never arose, although Gordon Aerolite was used in 30 Miles Magister tail planes at A.R.L. in 1939.

In 1937 glass fibre became available and DB saw its potential and asked for samples for use with resin. The suppliers said they saw no prospect of it being suitable for moulded plastics! Glass reinforced plastics are now widely used. Another A.R.L. project related to sandwich construction, using cores of balsa or honeycomb between two sheets of aluminium.

In a DB notebook of 1938 is a sketch of an idea for using hexagonal honeycomb in an aircraft tail plane. The development of 'Redux' metal adhesive opened up metal to metal aircraft construction and a variety of sandwich constructions.

'Redux', a metal adhesive, was derived from the Gordon Aerolite work. Its first practical use was bonding clutch linings in wartime tanks, giving ten times the life of riveted linings. The first aircraft use involved bonding Duralumin to plywood in a folding wing hinge mechanism. Redux and its derivatives are now very widely used in aircraft – and indeed in many other industries world wide.

After the war A.R.L. grew, becoming part of Ciba in 1947. With capital investment further expansion was substantial, including adding Ciba's Araldite epoxy resin production and sales to the Duxford site.

At the 25 year anniversary celebrations in May 1959 DB announced his intention to resign as MD at the end of 1960. One retirement presentation to him was the propeller of the Snark. Retirement never really happened, though, as he went on to involve himself in developments at Techne.

His 90th birthday will evoke many memories ....He regularly opened the A.R.L. mail, adding succinct but helpful comments on letters to be dealt with by others; or, kneeling at a desk in the first available office, he would hand write a full but brief reply to his own mail. Hearing that I was to have my tonsils out, he drove me to Addenbrookes, saw me safely ensconced and arranged for his driver to collect me some days later. One could go on. Suffice it to say Happy Birthday, DB – from all of us.

Paul Dunn,
Duxford Chatterbox, Issue 184 (November 1994), pp 14-15.

APPENDIX ONE

THE ESTABLISHMENT AND DEVELOPMENT OF AERO RESEARCH LIMITED[47]

INTRODUCTION

Each week during the academic year Professor Edwards exhibits a fish he has caught of a species whose activities may be of interest to economists.

Though uncomfortable for the fish which is unaccustomed to gulp so much academic air, and dislikes its public dissection, it must be a service to human knowledge to find out what makes these creatures 'tick', and whether their behaviour is, in fact, at all comparable with that ascribed to them by economists.

Like most of my fellow fish, I know very little about economics, but in an endeavour to catch up I had a look recently at some of the simpler books in the Marshall Library at Cambridge, and they all seemed to base their analyses on the principle that business men are motivated by a desire to maximise their profits.

With that mock humility displayed by amateurs who make suggestions to professionals, I would like to ask whether this principle is not really a special case of a more general one motivating not only business men, but everyone else too – the desire to maximise enjoyment of life. An economic system erected on this basic principle might represent a considerable step forward because it would include all the activities of business men that are wrongly described as irrational, such as spending their money on office gadgets or entertaining their secretaries. There would still, of course, be room for Robinsonian equations which would, at least in the formal sense, reduce to order the subject of imperfect enjoyment.

47. Originally published in Ronald S. Edwards and Harry Townsend (eds), *Business Enterprise*, London 1958.

Pursuing the fish simile, you will, no doubt, observe that the present specimen is a coelacanth, rather unhappy in the shallow waters of cybernetic existentialism in which today it has to swim. I was brought up in the creed of Samuel Smiles which said that if an individual had a good idea and worked hard, he would both gain the respect of the community and enough money to go and do better. Or in Dr Johnson's words – There are few ways in which a man can be more innocently employed than in getting money.' That creed, I am told, only applies in the early days of an expanding capitalist economy; it disappears just as soon as clever Wykehamists or brilliant Oxford dons, or worse still, those politicians who are both of these things, can influence voters to give themselves immediate benefits without over much regard to the future.

But it is a fact that the most progressive economies in the free world such as those of Switzerland and of the United States, two countries which I visit fairly frequently, are both imbued with an old-fashioned 'Samuel Smiles' spirit. And it is such countries that are increasingly financing the newer industries of the UK. I recently made a survey of the British plastics and rubber industries and was surprised at the extent to which they are in fact American industries.

As regards Switzerland, I cannot improve on what Professor Edwards wrote in 1949 in his *Industrial Research in Switzerland.*:

There is still a powerful incentive to earn income in Switzerland and enough of it can be retained to maintain the momentum of industrial development. (p 66)

The lessons that Switzerland has to offer are almost platitudinous, but none the easier to accept for all that. The high general level of her industrial achievement is not due to exceptional intellectual qualities, nor to more extensive research than occurs in other major industrial countries, nor to spectacular feats of organisation, nor to unusually brilliant administration. The Swiss, like other people, can point to successes in all these directions, but the real key to their industrial ability lies first and foremost in the attitude of the people. They are poor in resources, they face up to this and to the fact that in a hard world the poor receive only what they work for. Their economy is based on a foundation of good education, both general and technical, and a belief in Samuel Smiles. The result is diligence, thoroughness, and conscientiousness in development and production, a steadily maintained and intelligent effort at the level of the individual factory from the labourer to the managing director. It may sound pedestrian and not at all like a Brave New World. But it enables the Swiss to achieve a high material standard of living.

THE ESTABLISHMENT OF AERO RESEARCH LTD

The establishment of Aero Research Ltd was not the result of a long, cool detached market research, or of a careful statistical sampling of public opinion. It was a red-hot idea that arose out of a youthful passion for flying and making aeroplanes, plus a conviction that is now a platitude – that a scientist could do a good job in industrial research. The idea was that there was room for a freelance research organisation by which I could carry my scientific work at Cambridge into industry and particularly aeronautics.

First of all we wanted plenty of space for an aerodrome and for future growth, and as farm land was then cheap and I was lucky enough to have some private resources, I bought a field at Duxford, about nine miles south of Cambridge. Aero Research Ltd was registered with offices at Duxford in 1934, although for three years before that it had, in fact, existed in a shed in Cambridge under the name of the Cambridge Aeroplane Construction Company. It is rather difficult to recall now how completely in the doldrums British aircraft design was in, say 1930. Thick wings were thought to have enormous drag, cantilever wings were thought to be too heavy; roughly speaking, anything but a biplane was regarded as un-English and not really practical. The British motor industry has in recent years, I think, been passing through a similar phase of complacency. I hope it won't get the bashing the British aircraft industry got from the DC-3 and its successors.

Like the man amazed to find he talked nothing but prose, I soon found that I had started something which from that day to this has never ceased to keep me hopping with surprises, occasional triumphs, near disasters, and a never-ending succession of problems, and though the scale has changed, it is, I am afraid, showing no signs of 'letting up' as the years roll by, though outwardly we may look more respectable and dignified.

We were successful in obtaining research contracts from de Havilland Aircraft Co. Ltd. I look back on those days with great satisfaction. They were good times and not least for the many remarkable men with whom I came into contact, such as Sir Geoffrey de Havilland, Mr Walker, Sir Bennet Melvill Jones, Sir David Pye and others. Later on we also worked for the Air Ministry and the Ministry of Aircaft Production.

Now bank managers will tell you that nothing is so foolish as to start a new and small business, and on the statistical facts they are right.

It is generally considered that not many small firms survive their first three years. If you listen to good advice you will not start a small business, but remember, all advice is bad, and good advice is fatal. The more you wrap up, the less fun you will have.

The records of the Bankruptcy Courts show that the usual reasons for the failure of small businesses are (1) incompetence, and (2) lack of capital. They account, I think, for about two-thirds of the failures. Well, we need not be incompetent, but the best of us can lack capital and it is a great difficulty.

Goodwill. But I think an equally great difficulty in building up a small firm is the difficulty of acquiring 'Goodwill', not only in the accountant's sense, but in its wider meaning defined as 'that which makes the old customer go to the old firm', a definition that makes clear under what a disadvantage a new company is.

This difficulty is, of course, one that really besets nearly every one of us. The slowness with which genius is recognised is proverbial, and the way in which the 'old men', whether they are academicians or established firms, 'get away' with inferior stuff, is galling and must be so to any right-minded young man.

Capital. However, one must not underestimate the difficulties resulting from lack of capital, needed not only for the plant and equipment, but also for two purposes which are sometimes overlooked – (1) working capital and (2) something to tide over the losses that in the first few years are almost inevitable, because production in a competitive economy must precede demand. It is a bit of a surprise to the beginner in business that the more successful he is, the worse his cash position gets, because cash is swallowed up in working capital and, in these days of penal taxation, it is very difficult to acquire capital rapidly enough from trading.

SANDWICHES AND HONEYCOMBS[48]

How should one choose the right material to make the lightest possible structure of given dimensions and strength?

This is quite a limited objective because in practice a structure is usually required to fulfil other requirements as well; in chemical engineering resistance to corrosion may predominate over all other considerations and in building construction thermal insulation may be the prime requisite. Nevertheless the problem of making an object of given dimensions, such as a chair or an aeroplane, as light as possible without sacrifice of strength is a fundamental one which if solved frequently also satisfies economic and even aesthetic requirements.

The principles which make possible a rational comparison of the suitability of structural materials, though to some extent understood by Galileo (see 'On Growth and Form' by D'A.W. Thompson[49]) were probably first clearly given by James Thomson, elder brother of Lord Kelvin, in a paper read in 1875 to the Institute of Engineers and Shipbuilders in Scotland entitled 'Comparisons of similar structures as to elasticity, strength and stability.'[50] The extension and application of these principles to the practical urgencies of aircraft design is due to Professor H. Wagner who in 1928[51] introduced the use of a quantity which has come to be known as 'the structure loading coefficient'. This structure loading is a measure of the load on a structure in relation to its size; it is one of those useful concepts like 'wing loading' or 'power loading' which enable the

48. Based on articles published in the *Aeroplane* and *Aircraft Engineering,* 1939.

49. D'Arcy W. Thompson, *On Growth and Form,* Cambridge 1942, Chapter 2.

50. James Thomson, 'Comparisons of Similar Structures as to Elasticity, Strength and Stability', Institute of Engineers and Shipbuilders in Scotland, 1875.

51. H. Wagner Zeits f., *Moter* (1928), p. 241; also *Aeroplane* 30 November 1939, p. 669. Sir Richard Southwell drew my attention to the fact that W. C. M. Pettingil originated the concept in R&M Q918, 1924.

human brain to comprehend the significance of several variables simultaneously

TENSION

The fundamental types of load on a structure are tension and compression. Shear, torsion and bending are due to combinations of tension and compression. For a material for a member subjected only to tensile forces specific failing stress (rupture load per unit area of cross section divided by specific gravity) is an important characteristic. This ratio is numerically equal to the length of a uniform rod of the material which is just sufficient to break in tension under its own weight; for this reason the ratio is often called the 'breaking length' and is measured in miles, kilometres, inches or other units of length. A table of breaking lengths is given below.

'Gordon Aerolite' owes it strength largely to its flax reinforcement. None of the organic materials (e.g. wood) are, in practice, as good in tension as the above table might suggest however because of the trouble of making effective end connections. For this reason the metals are probably the best tension materials. Unfortunately while tension is easily dealt with there are few structures where only tension has to be considered because tension must necessarily give rise to compression somewhere else if equilibrium is to exist. Spiders and çivil engineers (sometimes) can shelve their responsibilities of looking after compressive loads (Fig. 1) but designers of aircraft and other self contained structures cannot.

COMPRESSION

The difficulties arising from compressive loads and of choosing the lightest material for a strut (i.e. a member under compression) are due to the fact that the rigidity of the member under load as well as the compressive strength of the material of which it is composed must be taken into account. As C. C. Walker pointed out in one of our Friday afternoon talks, a bicycle spoke is an example of a member designed to take tension only. It does the job remarkably well and will sustain say half a ton in tension irrespective of its length.

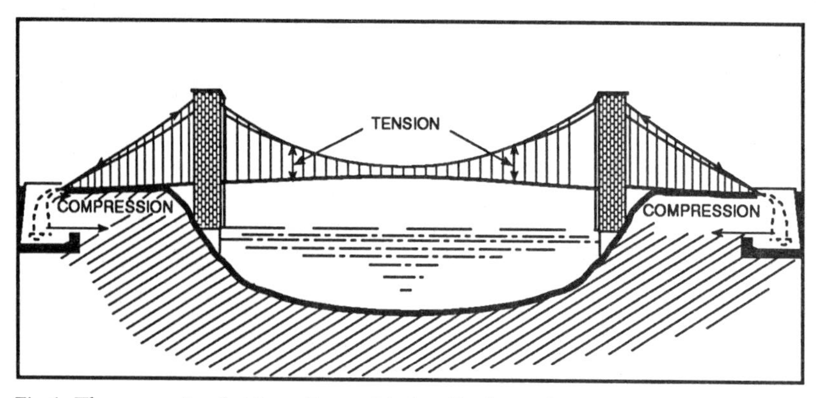

Fig 1. The suspension bridge relies on Mother Earth to take compression

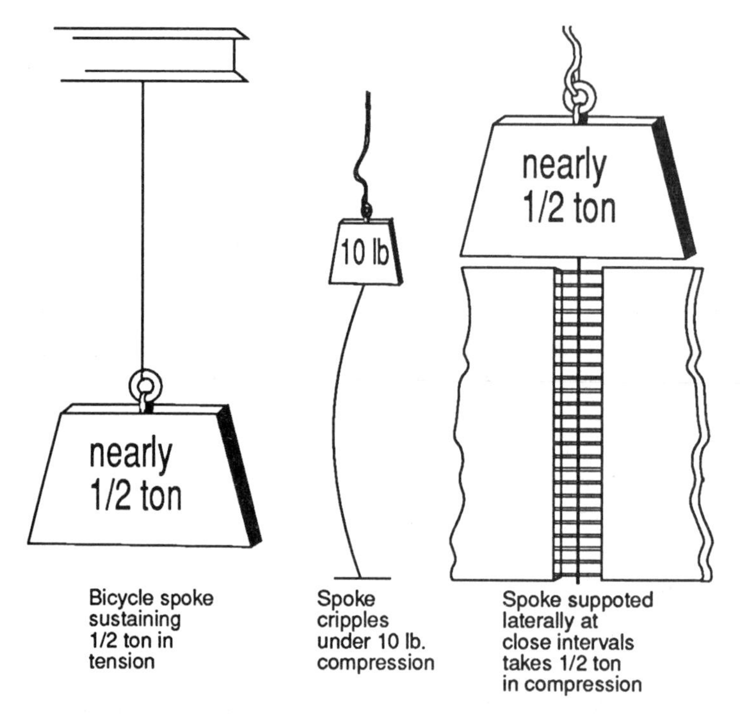

Fig. 2

But if we apply even ten pounds in compression it buckles and tries to dodge the load. (Fig 2). It is clearly no good at all as a compression member. It will however stand up to a compressive load of

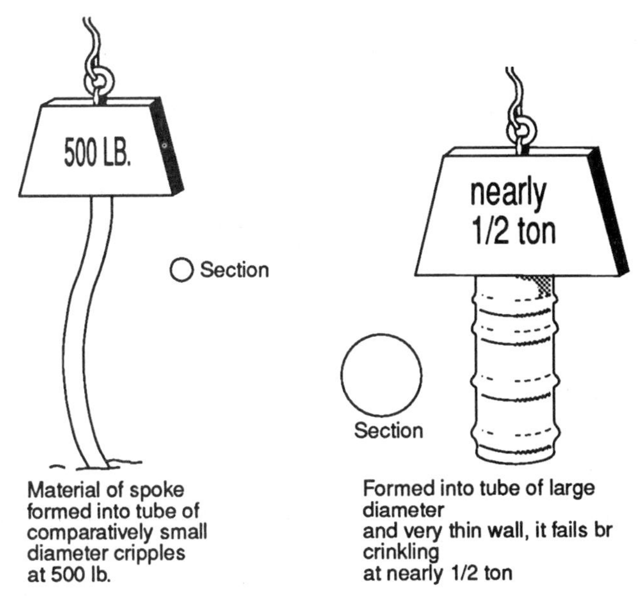

Fig. 3.

Material	Breaking Length
Carbon fibre reinforced plastic	
Flax fibre	96 kilometres
Silk fibre	49 kilometres
'Gordon Aerolite'	32 kilometres
Aluminium Alloy (30 tons/in^2)	17 kilometres
Stainless Steel (80 tons/in^2)	16 kilometres
Spruce (4.5 tons/in^2)	14 kilometres

nearly half a ton if we reduce its length considerably, so that if we support the spoke sufficiently well, we can make it into an efficient strut.

This expedient is used in every rolled steel joist where the compression flange is stabilised by the web fixed in turn to the tension flange. Unfortunately there is not always a convenient adjacent tension member to provide stabilisation, but there is another way. A tube can be formed of the spoke material so as to have the same weight as the spoke, such a tube will be able to withstand quite a high load, say 500 pounds, before collapsing by buckling.

We can obtain more stabilisation against 'buckling failure' by increasing the diameter of the tube further, but as the weight is kept constant the wall thickness must be correspondingly thinner and at certain ratio of wall thickness to radius 'crinkling failure' occurs as shown in Fig. 3.

The most efficient strut we can make is one which is expanded to the limit where crinkling sets in. It frequently happens (as in the fuselage of an aeroplane) that the diameter and length of the tube are so great and the applied load relatively so low (in other words the 'structure loading' is so low) that an efficient metal strut of such dimensions would at once be too strong and too heavy. In such a case we have to make the best of a bad job by making the skin so thin that it carries very little direct compressive load and then stiffen it with longitudinal stiffeners and stabilising rings. In effect we concentrate on loads so as to get locally increased structure loading on the stiffeners. This is what designers of all-metal fuselages have to do; it is not an elegant solution and in principle it is far better to use a less dense material.

Figs. 2 and 3 (due to C. C. Walker) are good illustrations of a fundamental principle of constructional engineering – the longer a strut in relation to the load it has to carry the more we have to 'expand' it (either geometrically or by using materials of lower density or both) if we are to obtain the greatest strength for the least weight.[52]

Consider for example the pylons which carry the 'Grid' wires over the countryside. They have to be tall to keep the wires clear of obstructions but the load they have to carry is small in relation to their size. Quite rightly therefore they are not solid objects but are highly articulated structures (Fig. 4); by the same argument the Nelson monument may be said to be an uneconomical solution of the problem of sustaining the weight of a statue 145 feet above ground, whatever its merits as a memorial.

THE ADVANTAGES OF SANDWICHES

Whenever the structure loading is low it is advantageous to make a sandwich structure in which metal is used for the ties and wood for the struts.

52. N. A. de Bruyne, *British Plastics*, Vol. 14 (November 1942), pp. 306–16.

Fig. 4 The Nelson memorial in Trafalgar Square is an uneconomical structure.

Sandwich panels made of metal cover plates with a light weight filling (or middle layer) are also of value wherever it is desirable to obtain maximum stiffness in bending for minimum weight, as in table tops, floors, walls, partitions and loud speaker diaphragms. If the sandwich is correctly proportioned it will have a better stiffness-to-weight ratio than that of panels of its constituent materials used alone; thus a correctly designed sandwich with duralumin cover plates and a plywood middle layer will be 8.3 times as stiff as a duralumin panel of the same weight, and 1.3 times as stiff as a plywood panel of the same weight. In Tables 1 and 2 below[53] the best ratio (R) of thickness of middle layer to thickness of one cover plate, as well; as the relative stiffness in bending, are given for a number of composite panels, all of the same weight (w) in pounds per square inch.

53. N. A. de Bruyne, *British Plastics*, Vol. 14 (November 1942), pp. 306–16.

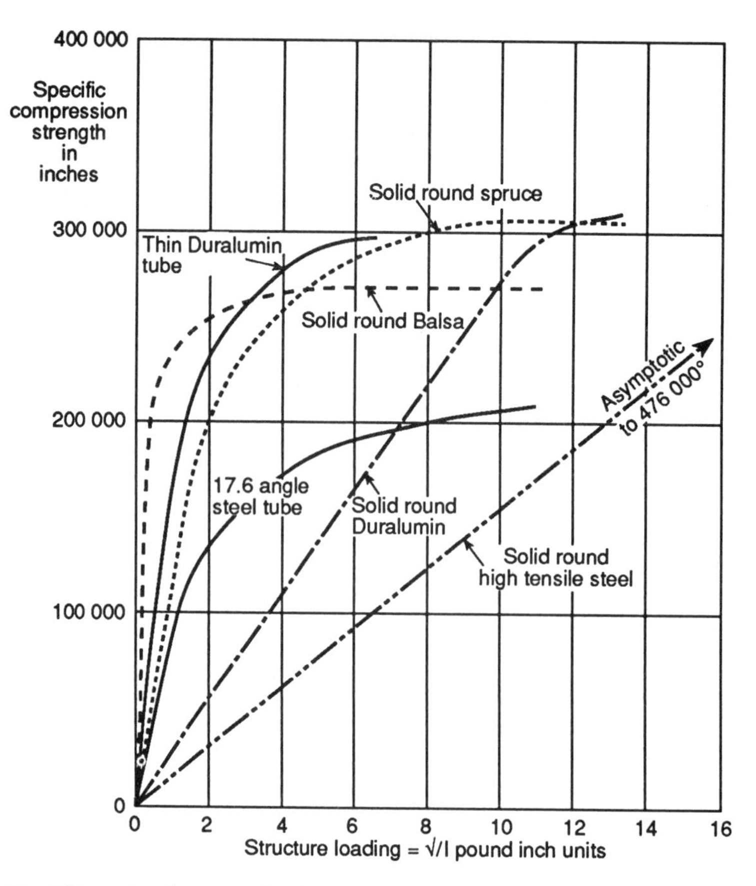

Fig. 5 Example of structure loading chart

THE STRUCTURE LOADING COEFFICIENT

The structure loading coefficient provides a means of measuring load in relation to length. It is the square root of the applied load divided by the length of the strut. The length of a chair leg is about 16 inches; if we take the weight of a man as 160 pounds and allow an arbitrary load factor of 5 then each leg will be required to sustain a load of 200 pounds. On these assumptions therefore the structure loading on a chair leg will be $\sqrt{200}/16=9$ pound inch units of structure loading.

If we now have a chart of the type shown in Fig. 6 where the structure loading is plotted along the X axis against the specific failing stress along the Y axis for different materials and different geometrical shapes we can at once see which material and form of cross section gives the highest specific failing stress for any given structure loading. We see at once wood is better than metal at low structure loadings while at high structure loadings the reverse is true, because the curve for 60 ton steel will, at a sufficiently high structure loading, reach a specific compressive strength of 60 x 2240/.282 = 476,000" which is much in excess of the ultimate strength of spruce.

Fig. 5 is of course of the nature of an example only. It would clearly be possible to draw in curves for I sections, for tubes of such dimensions that they fail simultaneously by bowing and crinkling, for magnesium alloys, and so on. Moreover Fig. 5 deals with struts, whereas usually we are frequently interested in panels and shells; but the same kind of principles can be applied (see H. Wagner 'Luftwissen' p.18, December 1938) using a slightly different form of expression for the structure loading.

Nevertheless Fig. 5 illustrates the truth of some general rules as follows:

(1) For compressive structure loadings of 12 and more and for all values of tensile load use metal in a solid or only slightly articulated form.
(2) For medium structure loadings use solid wood or light alloys in tubular or similar form.
(3) For structure loading less than 2 use wood either as a solid balsa or in the form of routed spruce sections or as a com posite 'sandwich' material.

Incidentally if our estimate of 90 for the structure loading on a chair leg is correct it would appear to be always possible to make a stronger chair in wood for the same weight or a lighter one for the same strength as one made from 17 G Mild Steel Tubing.

Comparison of the stiffness of the sandwiches listed in Tables 1 and 2 in comparison with that of the constituents in Table 3 shows the value of the sandwich structure in obtaining a high value of stiffness for a given weight. In addition such sandwiches possess the

Table 1 Sandwich Structure with Cover Plates of Steel

Middle Layer	R	Flexural stiffness compared with that of plain steel	Thickness of a panel weighing w lb per sq inch
Plywood	19.4	53.0	19.0 w inches
Reinforced plastic*	25.0	18.2	15.2 w inches
Cork (agglomerated)	100.0	329.0	63.8 w inches

Table 2 Sandwich Structure with Cover Plates of Duralumin

Middle Layer	R	Flexural stiffness compared with that of plain steel	Thickness of a panel weighing w lb per sq inch
Plywood	22.0	60.0	28.6 w inches
Reinforced plastic*	6.3	20.0	16.4 w inches
Balsa (along the grain)	571.0	approx. 5000.0	approx. 254.0 w inc
Cork (agglomerated)	36.0	297.0	64.0 w inches

Table 3 Simple Panels

Material	Flexural stiffness compared with that of steel panel of same weight	Thickness of a panel weighing w lb per sq inch
Steel	1.0	3.6 w inches
Duralumin	7.3	9.9 w inches
Plywood	46.0	34.5 w inches
Reinforced Plastic*	6.6	21.1 w inches
Balsa (along the grain)	approx. 4650.0	approx. 277.8 w inches
Cork (agglomerated)	1.3	95.2 w inches

* Fabric or paper laminated material made with a thermosetting resin.

desirable features of good thermal and acoustical insulation and a strong metallic surface to resist wear and abrasion.

BIOLOGICAL CONSIDERATIONS

It is extremely interesting to see how Nature deals with these problems of size and shape and Thomas McMahon (assistant professor of applied mechanics in the division of engineering and applied physics at Harvard) has shown that considerations of elastic stability and flexure of struts require living organisms (e.g. trees and animals) should adopt forms whereby lengths increase as the 2/3 power of the diameter.[54]

One can also observe that sandwich structures are used wherever advantageous and Claude Rayner in his *Milestones in the History of Ciba (ARL) Ltd.* writes:

> DB brought along an object for me to see, concealed under a blackboard duster with only a small section exposed to view. Here was a wonderful sight, the very structure we were aiming at, an integral skin on each side with here and there a decreasing density towards the centre. He removed the duster and there was a section of a human skull.[55]

SANDWICHES IN AIRCRAFT STRUCTURES[56]

No doubt C. C. Walker had a strong influence on the thinking of the design team in the choice of plywood-balsa sandwich construction in the little twin-engined 'Comet' in 1934, which was rushed through to win the air race to Melbourne, Australia. The same construction was used in the D.H. 91 Albatross airliner in 1937

54. Thomas McMahon, 'Size and Shape in Biology', *Science,* Vol. 179 (23 March 1973), pp. 1201–4.

55. C. A. A. Rayner, *Milestones in the History of CIBA (A.R.L.) Limited (1934–59),* Cambridge 1959.

56. I had already applied for a British Patent for a method of making a perforated metal spacer sheet, and now asked the British Patent Office to declare it a secret patent (no. 577790), which was immediately granted. However, publication in a British report, which made evident the value of the invention, was circulated and not kept secret (and noted in an American publication).

which was a vindication of C. C.Walker's argument for the economy resulting from high speed attained by aerodynamic cleanness.

The deflections of the wing tips were of course larger than in an all metal machine and it is said that after its first flight the pilot remarked on this to DH who replied that there was no need to worry as on test they had deflected three feet before breaking. The test pilot's comment was 'Yes, but they were deflecting two feet, eleven inches!' And of course this structure was used in the D.H. Mosquito, which triumphantly made nonsense of the pre-war policy of the Air Ministry.

It is interesting to note that Daniel Gooch used wood to reinforce metal sheets successfully in a series of locomotives made between 1840 and 1847 for the Great Western Railway. The main frames were of 'slotted sandwich pattern compounded of wooden slabs and thin iron plates bolted together'.[57]

STRENGTH OF SANDWICH PANELS

It is easy to compute the lateral stiffness of sandwich panels but it is a much more difficult problem to analyse the strength of a sandwich structure. I had come across a paper by a Swedish professor who had computed the effect of the surrounding earth on the stability of a pile as it is driven into the ground and asked G. S. Gough, my co-director of studies at Trinity whether it had any applicability to my problem He at once got interested and soon had produced a restricted solution which he later generalised. I roped in Mrs Tipper (a Fellow at Newnham College) and we took over the former kitchen of Scroope House, which also housed the library and offices of the Engineering Lab. The result was (1) wrinkles in the coverplates under compressive load (2) the wave length inverse proportionality to the cube root of the elastic modules of the material.Honeycombs – A joint paper by Gough, Tipper and myself was published. No one understood our work until years later. In brief Gough's analysis was confirmed.[58]

This suggested to me that (1) a mechanically reticulated structure should be efficient provided that the reticulations were smaller than

57. I am indebted to Mr R. F. G. Lea for this information.

58. G. S. Gough, C. F. Elam, and N. A. de Bruyne, 'The Stabilisation of a Thin Sheet by a Continuous Supporting Medium', *Journal of the Royal Aeronautical Society,* Vol. 44 (1940).

the wavelengths and (2) that almost any material could be used as a filling. I had already made such a structure in which a filling of phenol formaldehyde honeycomb reticulation was glued to phenol formaldehyde coverplates with an aniline formaldehyde glue (BP 577790 of 1938). The honeycomb filling was at right angles to the coverplates and differs in this respect from the honeycomb structure of H. N. Atwood (USP 2029214 of 1934) and the balsa sandwiches of the de Havilland Aircraft Co. BP 577790 of 1938 was declared secret and was not released until after the war when ICI opposed it. At that time I did not feel I had the time or money to proceed and told my patent agents, to their surprise, to drop it.

When USA joined in World War II there was a complete disclosure to the U.S. authorities of all British developments, including of course the Whittle jet engine. In 1952 I visited the Glenn L. Martin aircraft factory and saw honeycomb slabs being made and used on a large scale, and on the West coast Hexcel were making honeycomb by a different process. When I got back I decided to make aluminium honeycomb using Araldite for the core and Redux for the attachment of the coverplates where resistance to peeling is of paramount importance. Since then the 'Bonded Structures Division' at Duxford has grown steadily and has found wide use for diverse applications.

REDUX[59]

To make a strong glued joint it is necessary that the liquid glue (1) should 'wet' the solid surfaces, i.e. that its angle of contact with the solid should be zero and (2) should not break up on solidification. Condition (1) is a physical-chemical condition; good wetting is an outward and visible sign of strong interfacial forces and it is also an 'engineering' condition because it reduces stress concentrations at the boundaries of the solidified liquid. To avoid spontaneous break-up on solidification we can use an elastomeric glue which undergoes strain (such as elongation or compression) without much stress, or if we want to seal glass to that of the metal we can match the thermal expansion of the glass to that of the metal or we can make the metal so thin that it undergoes plastic deformation as the glass contracts (Housekeeper seal). We can also prevent spontaneous disruption on solidification by packing the liquid adhesive with a reinforcement such as glass fibre. In general, it is easier to glue porous materials like wood than to impervious materials like metals because porosity allows volatiles in the glue to escape.

When we were making components by pressing textiles soaked in phenoformaldehyde resin, we would sometimes be plagued by adhesion to the metal mould and when we were making Gordon-Aerolite (using linen reinforcement) the adhesion could be considerable. This led to make up a typical aircraft panel consisting of a duralumin sheet with longitudinal duralumin stiffeners glued on to it by means of a layer of Gordon-Aerolite between each stiffener and the sheet.

The effect of the textile reinforcement was obviously to strengthen the phenol formaldehyde (PF) resin but it was probably also permitting the water and other volatiles to escape from the joint. It

59. Based on a paper 'Pioneering Times' given in June 1980 to the Adhesives for Industry Technology Conference, El Segundo, California; and 'The Strengh of Glued Joints', *Aircraft Engineering*, Vol.16 (1944), pp 115-19, 140.

occurred to me to try 'Formvar', which is a thermoplastic material with a softening temperature higher than the other thermoplastics available at that time, in place of the Gordon-Aerolite, and which can soak up water and which has an affinity for PF resins. Initially we used films of Formvar, made by pressing Formvar powder between flat metal sheets, and applied the liquid PF resin to the 'adherends' (the parts to be joined). We got good joints in this way but George Newell[60] suggested that we do the job in one go by dusting the Formvar powder on the PF coated adherends and then applying heat and pressure to make the joint. This was simpler and gave stronger joints. It was on 4 December 1941 that we made a metal-to-metal joint with a shar strength of over 100 lb/in^2. We called the adhesive Redux (=Research at Duxford). For some purpose, this technique was not very suitable and we therefore also made a film from Reduc powder held together between two polythylene sheets coated with PF resin; this was made on a machine designed by my brother-in-law Robert Marsh. It employed non-contacting radio isotope gauges to control the thickness of the powder film. The polythene sheets were peeled off immediately before use. This film was also made with a reinforcement of glass fibre for gluing cover plates to honeycomb cores.

Initially, the breaking strengths of simple tensile-shear test specimens showed a wide scatter. But this was considerably reduced by etching the aluminium alloy (usually Alclad) in chromic acid.

We made up a compression test panel and sent to the RAE for testing. It surprised them and us; because it was stronger than another panel exactly similar except that it was a riveted structure.

I then exhibited a panel at an exhibition organised by the Society of British Aircraft Constructors in London in 1942. We also had on our stand a lot of small lap joints which people were invited to break; of course no one could. R. E. Bishop, chief designer of de Havilland Co., came to this exhibition and used Redux in the de Havilland 'Hornet' which was the fastest propeller driven aeroplane ever made. It was intended to be a replacement for the de Havilland 'Mosquito' and while it was mainly a wooden machine the tension flanges of the wing spars were made of duraluminum, bonded Redux, to plywood webs. The first practical use of Redux was not in aircraft but in tanks – in bonding several thousand clutches for

60. G. S. Newell, 'Metal Bonding', *Aero Research Technical Notes*, No. 116 (August 1952).

Cromwell and Churchill tanks, giving a life of between two and three thousand miles compared with two hundred for riveted clutches.

ADVANTAGES OF REDUX

The advantages of Redux bonding over conventional methods of joining light alloys are:[61]

1. Reduction in weight: thinner gauge metals can be used and reinforced where necessary (for example, round cut-outs and edges).
2. Increase in fatigue life: the effect of stress raisers can be reduced by local reinforcement.
3. Smooth external finish: a smooth external finish is obtained. Where rivets have to be used, as in final assembly, simple countersunk riveting is frequently made possible by thicken ing the skin locally on the inside.
4. Simplification of 'pressurisation': bonded joints simplify the problems presented by cabin 'pressurisation' and by integral tanks.
5. Reduction of production costs and time: an entire compo nent can be bonded in one operation. As soon as a compo nent exceeds a certain size, bonding becomes progressively cheaper than automatic riveting.
6. Simplification of design: in general, the designs of bonded structures are simpler than those of riveted structures.
7. Simplification of maintenance: the replacement of loose rivets is largely eliminated.
8. Increased strength: bonded joints have greater strength than comparable riveted or spot-welded joints.
9. New type of structure: the use of sandwich structures, such as those incorporating honeycomb cores, is made practicable by adhesive bonding. These advantages relate mainly to the superiority of bonding over riveting techniques but it should not be forgotten that the use of adhesives is also to be pre ferred to integral construction or machining out of the solid, which requires expensive equipment, entails a large amount

61. 'Redux – the First Twelve Years', *Aero Research Technical Notes,* No. 149 (May 1955).

of waste, and is more prone to the propagation of fatigue cracks than a laminated structure in which the amorphous glue layers act as 'crack stoppers'.

The 'Dove'.

The de Havilland 'Dove' (1946) was the first all-metal aircraft designed for bonding; Redux was used throughout for attaching stringers in the fuselage and wings as well as for local reinforcement.

By this time a number of results had been published on comparative tests carried out with riveted, spot-welded and Redux-bonded joints. Redux had provided consistently higher failing loads and de Havilland's own 'top-hat' stringers bonded with Redux would reach stresses up to 125 per cent of those developed by exactly similar panels with riveted and spot-welded joints.

Apart from improved strength, bonding provided the 'Dove' with aerodynamically clean external surfaces and enabled considerable savings to be made in production costs both of the 'Doves' and 'Herons'. In the 'Dove', it was established that the Redux bonding of stringers to skin was about one-third the cost of riveting.

The Naval Version of the 'Mosquito' and 'Hornet'.

The use of Redux bonding made possible the provision of folding wings in the 'Mosquito' and in the 'Hornet'.

The 'Comet'.

From the outset it was decided to use Redux on an ambitious scale in the 'Comet' This aircraft, which first flew in July 1949, would raise cruising speeds overnight by about 200 m.p.h. and much importance would therefore be attached to aerodynamically smooth surfaces. The high altitude flying would also pose problems of pressurisation which could be solved far more easily by bonding as opposed to riveting with its need for the subsequent sealing of each hole.

Most important of all, the use of Redux enabled enormous weight saving to be achieved without detriment to strength and its principal role was in fact to ensure an economic payload. Full details of the use of Redux in the 'Comet' were given by Mr H. Povey, director of Aircraft Production of the de Havilland Aircraft Company, in a paper on 'Planning and Production Methods Used in the Construction of the de Havilland "Comet"' presented to the Royal Aeronautical Society in April 1951.

Following on the accidents to G-ALYP and G-ALYY, a public enquiry was held at which adverse criticism was made of the use of Redux. On 1 February 1955, Lord Cohen (Commissioner) presented his report completely exonerating Redux as a cause of the accidents. In the 'Comet' 4, Redux was employed even more extensively than before for all longitudinal stringers of the fuselage shell, spanwise stringers in wings, aileron and flap structures, wall stiffeners in fin and elevators, for the canopy structure and seams of pressure dome and in many other structural applications.

THE FOKKER COMPANY

To the de Havilland Aircraft Company belongs the credit for their farsighted confidence in a revolutionary technique and it was some time before any other firm followed them. Probably the first to do so was the N.V. Koninklijke Vliegtuigenfabriek Fokker. Both de Havilland and Fokker companies were traditionally 'glue minded' as they both had made excellent aeroplanes with wooden structures.

The late Mr R. J. Schleikelmann, who was primarily responsible for the introduction of Redux at Fokker, subsequently wrote an excellent book on glued metal structures – *Gelijmde metalen Constructies*[62] Unfortunately it was never translated into English. By the use of Redux, the Fokker company was also able to avoid the use of structural components machined from the solid, which require the use of expensive equipment.

Mr Edw. van Beek, chief of structures at the Fokker Co., in an article published in 1955, in *Technique et Science Aeronautique*, gave an excellent review of Fokker experience and concludes by saying:

62. R. J. Schliekelmann, *Gelijmde metalen Constructies*, AGON-Elsevier, Amsterdam 1970.

> The main purpose of this paper is to point out that a new approach to structural design can be developed with the help of metal-bonding processes, taking full advantage of this new technique without incurring unnecessary risks. The examples shown indicate that a glued structure is not a riveted structure without the rivet lines replaced by glue lines, but has its own characteristics, whilst a powerful tool has become available in designing for fatigue.

In the 'Friendship' (F27) which was designed some twenty-five years ago and in other applications of Redux, the Fokker Company showed the brilliant expertise of artists who extend the possibilities and understand the limitations of their medium.

With Redux it became possible to make laminated metal structures.

> Using only simple production aids better results are achieved with this method than can be obtained with much greater difficulty by expensive milling methods. the correct use of this technique can lead to surprising results. By correct choice of the surface dimensions of the different layers it is possible to achieve the ideal of a completely uniform stress distribution in the structure. At the same time, the avoidance of stress raisers has a considerable influence on the life of components subject to fatigue loading...The forces prevailing in the highly loaded double bolt connection in the Fokker helicopter blade were successfully absorbed by the complex lamination of individual plates to form a single group. In the Fokker F-27, there are many examples of the laminating technique. The entire lower skin of the wing is made up of layers bonded in this way. As a result, it is possible to avoid stress concentrations due to the tensile stress in the vicinity of the connection between the inner and outer wing sections and around the tank cover apertures. Extended fatigue loading tests on these wing joints have shown that by these means the maximum theoretical mechanical strength was obtained. This was very satisfactory especially when using the copper-zinc alloy 75ST, which is sensitive to stress concentrations. The laminating method of construction is also successfully employed for the construction of the fuselage of the F-27, for example; to avoid stress concentrations at critical points around the window cut-outs in the pressure cabin.
>
> About five years later, another remarkable use was found for laminated constructions. Components with varying cross-section over their length, such as certain skin plates and especially the flanges or spars, were previously always produced using the expensive milling method. At Fokker, the idea was adopted of manufacturing these

components from thin plates of different lengths bonded together. In particular, long L- and T- flanges made from pre-formed L- plate sections were constructed. It was even found possible to post-form flat laminated layers with the aid of a rubber press to five L sections. This had no adverse effect on the static compression strength or on the fatigue life. For a period of a year the Dutch National Aircraft Research Establishment (NLL) in conjunction with Fokker carried out tests of the static and dynamic characteristics of this type of construction. The results showed that spars bonded together using the laminating method were, from the point of view of mechanical strength, equal in quality to solid components.

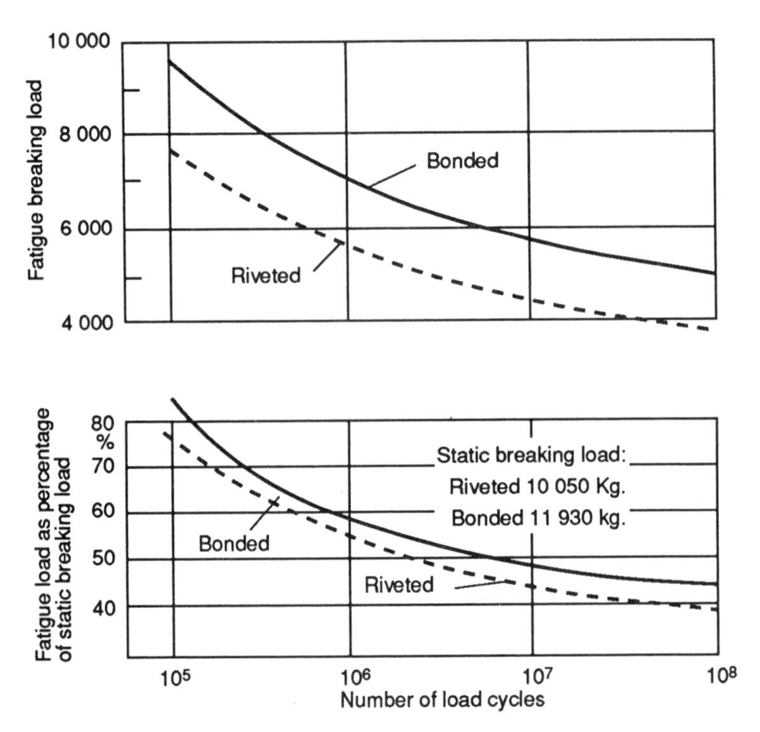

Fig. 6 Results of fatigue test on reinforced panels with stringers glued and riveted

STABILITY

In riveted joints, the forces to be transmitted are all at one point. The two components to be joined must, therefore, be rigid enough to transmit the forces concentrated at each rivet, but if the load is uniform as a result of using a film of glue, the components to be connected can be less rigid. Furthermore, with a layer of glue present, the two components support each other. The continuity provided by a glue joint gives much greater stability.

In Holland, considerable attention was paid to this point from the start. Comparative compression tests on plates with reinforcing members, either glued or riveted in place, indicated clearly the increase in mechanical strength obtained by bonded joints. When plates with riveted reinforcements were loaded, buckles occurred over the entire surface. The buckling extended over the surfaces between the rows of rivets and affected the rivets themselves. In the case of bonded reinforcements a completely different picture of buckle formation was produced. Distortion was completely uniform between the reinforcements, while over the reinforcing members themselves, the surfaces remained smooth. The buckles formed between the reinforcements were much smaller than in the riveted structure and the buckled areas were clearly separated from each other by the glue seams. This shows that a glued structure is more rigid than a riveted one. Accordingly, with glued structures a much higher breaking load is obtained than for riveted structures. The thinner the plate construction, the greater the difference in this respect between the two methods of manufacture . . .

The prevention of buckle formation has an important influence on life under fatigue loading. In riveted joints, cracks occur extremely quickly below the rivet heads at the edges of the buckled areas. On the other hand, with glued skin sections, the formation of the first crack is commonly observed after a life more than ten times as long, this crack being on the flanges of the glued-on reinforcement. The graphs in Fig. 6, illustrate this point.[63]

The Fokker-VEW B.V. wrote to me on 28 November 1978:

At present, nearly 800 Fokker F 27 aircraft (including 205 produced by Fairchild) have been sold. Your invention is still the most important bonding technique used by the Fokker Company. The 'Redux' system is also used in the Fokker F28 Fellowship programme, a civil short haul jetliner of which at present 150 aircraft have been sold.

63. R. J. Schliekelmann, 'Adhesive Bonding of Metals in Aircraft Production', *Aero Research Technical Notes,* No. 184 (April 1958).

For Elma
Jane de Glehn
1941.